The **Big Book** of
Caterpillar

The Complete History of Caterpillar Bulldozers and Tractors, Plus Collectibles, Sales Memorabilia, and Brochures

By Robert N. Pripps
Photographs by Andrew Morland
Foreword by Bob Feller, Caterpillar Collector

Japonica Press

Edited by Michael Dregni
Designed by Andrea Rud
Printed in Hong Kong

ISBN 09533 737 3 8

A catalogue record for this book is available from the British Library

First published in the United Kingdom in 2000 by
Japonica Press
Low Green Farm
Hutton
Driffield
East Yorkshire
YO25 9PX

Published in the United States by Voyageur Press, Inc., Stillwater, MN 55082 U.S.A.

Page 1 photos
Top: *1947 Caterpillar D4 U Series Orchard. Owner: Larry Maasdam.*
Center: *Three generations of Caterpillar machines. From right: 1912 Holt Sixty, 1928 2-Ton, and 1936 RD4. (Glenbow Archives)*
Bottom left: *1930s Caterpillar toy. Owner: Robert Stewart.*
Bottom right: *1940s Caterpillar dealer clock. Owner: Larry Maasdam.*

Pages 2–3, main photo: *1934 Caterpillar Diesel Seventy-Five. Owners: the Skirvin Brothers; Carl Skirvin is at the controls.*
Page 3, inset: *1920s Caterpillar magazine.*
Page 6: *1950s Caterpillar Orchard D2. Owner: Larry Maasdam.*

Dedication

For my newest grandson, Trajan Robert Pripps. He was born while I was in Clarion, Iowa, helping Andrew Morland get the pictures for this book. —Robert N. Pripps

Acknowledgments

This big book would be quite small if it were not for the contributions of the Caterpillar collectors you will meet in the following pages and for some helpful folks at Caterpillar, Inc.—namely Archivist Lee McCall, Public Affairs Director Jeff Hawkinson, Employee Information Manager Francis S. Duren, and Visitor Service Representative Mel Linden. Thanks also to Katherine Wright and Chuck Kilbreath of Patton Tractor and Equipment, Rockford, Illinois, a Caterpillar dealership. In addition, my thanks to Manfred Baedeker and Willy Soll of Claas KGaA in Germany.

The Antique Caterpillar Machinery Owner's Club officers and directors were also helpful, especially Dave Smith, Kent Bates, Larry Maasdam, and Marv Fery. The club's quarterly magazine provided a wealth of background information. Everyone seriously interested in historic Caterpillar should belong to the club. You can contact them at their International Business Office, Antique Caterpillar Machinery Owner's Club, 10816 Monitor-McKee Road, Woodburn, Oregon 97071 USA.

Collector Ed Claessen provided expert help and allowed me to copy many of his unique historical pieces of artwork.

Anyone who tries to write books of history naturally owes a debt to the historians who came before them, and this book is no different; I owe a debt to Reynold Wik, C. H. Wendel, Randy Leffingwell, Eric Orlemann, Jeff Creighton, and Bob LaVoie.

John Skarstad in the Department of Special Collections and Erin Brimmer in Illustration Services at the University of California–Davis provided some of the great historic images from the Eastman collection. My special thanks to them.

For other images, thanks to John Allen of J. C. Allen & Son and Stan Cohen of Pictorial Histories Publishing Company.

Thanks to my friends at the Park Falls, Wisconsin, public library for research help and for ordering books. Thanks also to Park Falls Print and Copy for special photocopying done while I waited.

Thanks to Bob and Anne Feller for his foreword to this book, and to Ralph W. Sanders for the use of his photograph of Bob.

Finally, thanks to my long-suffering wife Janice for bearing with me while I ensconced myself in front of the computer for hours and hours.

For comments and corrections, please communicate with me through the publisher, or via e-mail at cen49867@centurytel.net.

Robert N. Pripps

Contents

Caterpillar Hall of Fame

By Bob Feller, Baseball Hall of Famer and Caterpillar Collector

---

Above: 1980 Caterpillar D8K brochure

Left: Bob Feller and his 1929 Caterpillar Twenty
Baseball Hall of Famer Bob Feller spent many hours at the controls of a Caterpillar Twenty while growing up in the 1930s on his family's farm in Van Meter, Iowa. Today, his Cat collection includes this Twenty and several other crawlers. (Photograph © Ralph W. Sanders)

1913 Holt
This early gas-engine-powered Holt featured crawler half-tracks and a tiller-style front wheel for steering. Owners: Larry Maasdam and Ron Miller.

1935 Caterpillar Diesel Fifty
Essentially the same tractor as the gas Fifty, the Diesel Fifty made its debut in 1933, and production continued through 1936. Owner: Robert Stewart.

When my father bought the first Caterpillar tractor in Iowa in the early 1930s to use on our family farm, everybody said he was crazy. "It won't work," folks told him. People in our part of the country drove Fordsons or Farmalls, Johnny Poppers or Olivers—tractors with wheels on them. Nobody used a Caterpillar with those crazy crawler treads on them. It simply wasn't *right*.

Well, naturally they were all wrong. That Cat Twenty proved itself on our farm and made a convert of me and many another farmer.

Our family's farm was located in the countryside near Van Meter in the south-central part of the state. Working our land, I put in many hours at the controls of that Cat Twenty, as well as the twelve-foot Caterpillar combine that my dad purchased to run with it. They were solid machines that served us well for many years. My fascination with Caterpillars grew from those roots and continues to grow today.

I left the family farm to earn my living throwing baseballs. When I was seventeen years old in 1936, I made my major league debut pitching for the Cleveland Indians against the St. Louis Cardinals. Over the years, I dueled from the pitching mound with some of the all-time greats, batters such as Ted Williams and Joe DiMaggio—just me against them. Some of the veterans of those days said I threw the fastest pitches they had ever seen.

We all took time out from baseball during the World War II years; I served with the U.S. Navy aboard the USS Alabama from December 1941 to August 1945. I returned to the mound in 1945 and remained true to the Cleveland Indians until my retirement from baseball in 1956. At the end of eighteen years of throwing fastballs for the Indians, I had a record of 266 wins against 162 losses, a lifetime ERA of 3.25, and 2,581 strikeouts. In 1962, I was elected to the Baseball Hall of Fame.

But despite my achievements on the baseball fields, part of my heart still belonged to the farm fields of my youth. Nostalgia for hallmarks of our roots seems to hit us harder as we grow older. For me, as for many farmers, one of the ties to my youth was the Caterpillar Twenty that I operated as a kid in the 1930s. I decided I wanted to track down another Twenty, which I soon did. Little did I know, but my life as a Cat collector had begun.

Since finding the Twenty, my small Caterpillar collection continues to grow. It's kind of my own personal Caterpillar "hall of fame" that includes my favorite Cat models: the Twenty, two Tens, a Forty, Twenty-Two, Twenty-Five, Twenty-Eight, and a D4. Someday soon I hope to add to the collection.

You can look at the latest Caterpillar today and see the history in the machine. The lineage of the Holt and Best machines, the steam age, perfection of the crawler system, the early gas tractors, and Cat's industry-leading development of diesel power are all in a modern Cat. And that's part of what makes the Caterpillar story so great.

Another aspect of Caterpillar's greatness is that the machines are so versatile, a fact that is shown in the roster of Cat collectors. We come from all walks of life. Some come from a farming background. Other people's fascination with Cats started while working with them on construction sites, logging crews, road-grading jobs—anything and everything a Caterpillar can do.

I don't think I need to explain the fascination of Caterpillars to anyone holding this new book in their hands. Veteran tractor author Robert N. Pripps and photographer Andrew Morland tell the story of Caterpillar's great history, beginning with its early farming and logging days in California at the hands of Benjamin Holt and Daniel and C. L. Best. There have been other good books published on Caterpillar in the past and there certainly will be more in the future, but *The Big Book of Caterpillar* stands out in its scope, in-depth coverage, and beautiful photographs and illustrations. I hope Caterpillar fans everywhere enjoy it.

1935 Caterpillar Diesel Forty
This Diesel Forty was used for snowplowing by Woodland Township, Minnesota. The crawler had a long career, clearing snow-covered roads as recently as 1965.

The Caterpillar Mystique

Above: Holt advertisement, 1917

This ad for Holt's Model 45 and 60 touted the benefits of the Caterpillar for logging and freighting. Freighting was a popular use for crawlers in the days before heavy-duty trucks.

Left: C. L. Best 60 hauling logs, 1920s

A crawler pulls more than its own weight in lumber out of the Canadian woods. (Glenbow Archives)

In the winter of 1923, my father, Raymond Pripps, took a job with a small logging operation owned by a man named Dave Emerson. Emerson had the logging rights to some of the last of the big pines in northern Wisconsin near Bearskull Lake in Springstead, Wisconsin. Emerson and his crew were to harvest the pines and sleigh-haul the logs to the nearest railhead, which was in the town of Powell, Wisconsin. To pull the sleighs, Emerson purchased a 10-Ton Holt crawler tractor. Dad was hired as one of the two drivers for the twenty-mile round trip. He made two round trips during the night, the other driver made two during the day. At each end of the journey, the Holt was refueled and greased.

The Holt did eighty miles per day, six days a week for two winters. Emerson had fifteen sleighs. Five were being loaded at Bearskull Lake while five were being unloaded into rail cars at Powell and the last five were in transit behind the Holt. I remember Dad saying that when the fuel was good and the Holt's engine was in tune, that there was six or so inches of blue flame flaring out above the exhaust pipe. I can just imagine it: A dark night with the stars so bright you can almost feel them; the husky rumble of the big un-muffled four-cylinder engine; the clank of the tracks; the crisp cold of a Wisconsin winter night; and six inches of blue flame spouting from the exhaust pipe!

To some, Dad's job would have been incredibly boring. To Dad, it was the best job he ever had. Today, there are a growing number of us, also infected with the romance of the big Cats, that would agree with him.

Three years ago, while visiting the Caterpillar plant in Peoria, Illinois, with members of the Antique Caterpillar Machinery Owners Club (ACMOC), a giant D11 came rumbling down the factory line on its way to the shipping lot. As it went by, one of the club members looked up at the driver and mused, "Do you suppose he's being paid to do that?"

That comment sums up what Andrew Morland and I tried to capture in this book—the mysterious attraction that some of us have for these machines, whether used in logging, farming, or construction.

Ghost of a Caterpillar D8
Like a monument in an unattended graveyard, this radiator and engine from a Caterpillar D8 tell a tale of long life and hard work.

Chapter I

The Promised Land

The Creation of the Best and Holt Companies, 1852–1890

Above: 1889 Daniel Best steamer and harvester engraving

Left: **Daniel Best steam traction engine, 1894**
Lumberjacks pause while hauling a gigantic load of monstrous logs behind their Daniel Best steamer. Best made fine use of his own name in advertising his machines as "The Best." (Eastman Collection, University of California–Davis)

Two family names—Holt and Best—are forever linked to the great name of Caterpillar. The Holt and Best families were typical of the farsighted people who arose during the Industrial Revolution with the ingenuity, ambition, and charismatic leadership skills that gave birth to formative industries. Alongside John and Charles Deere, the McCormick family, William Deering, James Oliver, Henry Ford, Daniel Massey, Alanson Harris, and James G. Cockshutt, the Holt and Best families played key roles in mechanizing agriculture and construction work. These individuals not only changed our way of life, they changed the world.

The Opening of the American West

North America of the mid-1800s would be virtually unrecognizable to most of us today. The American Civil War had not yet been fought and slavery was still a fact of life in parts of the United States. Rail transportation was generally available only along the East Coast; in 1869, the Golden Spike was driven in Promontory, Utah, finally connecting Sacramento, California, and the West Coast to much of the rest of the country. The first commercial telegraph message was sent in 1844, the telephone was invented in 1876, and the light bulb followed in 1879. The culture and industry of North America were on the verge of rapid expansion.

In January 1848, carpenter James W. Marshall was building a waterwheel-powered sawmill for John A. Sutter in California's Sacramento Valley when he discovered gold. Marshall oversaw a crew of forty Native Americans who were digging the mill race. As Marshall remembered the event, "It was my custom in the evening to raise the gate and let the water wash out as much sand and gravel through the night as possible, and in the morning I would walk down and, shutting off the water, look along the race to see what was to be done. One morning my eye was caught with the glimpse of something shining at the bottom of the ditch. There was about a foot of water running there. I reached my hand down and picked it up; it made my heart thump, for I was certain it was gold. The piece was about the size and shape of a pea. Then I saw another piece in the water. After taking it out I sat down and began to think hard."

During the next days, the carpenter located more gold. Finally, on the twenty-eighth day, he went to the ranch to show John Sutter what he had found. Sutter made him promise to keep the discovery a secret, but the news leaked out. Within a few days, prospectors were heading up the Sacramento River by boat to look for gold, and San Francisco became almost a ghost town as the populace went prospecting.

By the end of the summer of 1848, news of Californian gold spread from the West Coast to the East Coast, to Mexico, and even to Hawaii. Newspapers claimed that folk had become rich overnight just by reaching down and picking up nuggets. People from all walks of life and all corners of the globe set out for California. By January 1849, a full-scale gold rush was on, and because of the date, the gold seekers were known as Forty-Niners.

There were also other riches waiting in the West. The forests held gold in the form of timber, while Northern California's Central and San Joaquin Valleys were ideal

Holt steamers and harvesters, circa 1910
A team of four Holt steamers with combined harvesters harvest rolling wheatfields in central California in this painting by artist Ben Sharpsteen. The couple in the foreground are attempting to restart their Locomobile. (Higgins Collection, University of California–Davis)

for mechanized wheat farming. Level, fertile soil produced wheat yields of two or even three times as many bushels per acre as those back East. The land beckoned.

Like many before him, the golden opportunities in the West lured nineteen-year-old Samuel Best, the eldest of sixteen children. In 1852, Samuel traveled from Iowa to Oregon to set up a sawmill, work he had previously done in Ohio and Missouri. Samuel's father, John, had used profits from the family sawmills to purchase 400 acres (160 hectares) of Iowa farmland near Keokuk, where the family made its home. Samuel sent letters back to the family extolling the benefits of life on the Western frontier.

In 1859, twenty-one-year-old Daniel Best followed his brother's trek. He worked his way to Washington as a wagon train guard and meat hunter, and then settled first in Walla Walla, just across the state line from Oregon. Here, and later in several other Washington and Oregon locations, he owned or operated sawmills.

Two more Best brothers, Henry and Zechariah, came West in 1861. In the Marysville–Yuba City area of north-central California, they took up wheat farming, a trade they knew from their days in Iowa. In 1870, Daniel moved to Marysville to help his brothers with what had become vast wheat ranches. When Henry became ill, Daniel took over operation of his ranch.

Birth of the Best Manufacturing Company

During the wheat harvest, Daniel Best was frustrated by the need to haul all of his grain to a Marysville grain-cleaning establishment. The Marysville company's mechanical device winnowed the grain and fanned away the chaff. Best felt that this consumed valuable time, and that the cost of hauling and cleaning was too high.

Best set about making his own portable grain cleaner that winter. After this machine was perfected, he constructed two more, which he planned to use to do custom cleaning at neighboring farms. To operate the cleaners, he also made "horsepowers," treadmills upon which horses walked to power machinery. The next fall, Daniel, Henry, and Zechariah Best earned some $200 daily with each machine, a handsome sum in 1871.

These earnings provided the seed money for Daniel to start the Best Manufacturing Company in Oakland, California, in 1871. Best's new outfit began making the newly patented grain cleaners in earnest. By 1884, the company bought the quarters of a former plow maker in San Leandro, California, and the firm's name was changed to Daniel Best Agricultural Works.

Daniel Best next turned his attention to grain harvesting. The dry California climate and stump-free, level terrain were favorable to the use of "headers" to harvest grain. A header used a cutter bar and reel, similar to that used in a binder, but cut off only the head of the grain,

leaving most of the stalk. A drive wheel called a "ground wheel" drove the pitman arm, reel, and "draper," also known as a conveyor. So the grain was not trampled, the header machine was pushed by a team of up to eight horses. The driver stood on a platform at the rear of the machine, where he controlled the horses and operated the steering wheel and brake. The cut grain was carried up the elevator and deposited in a wagon that was pulled alongside the header by a separate team, which then took the grain to a thresher. Although header harvesting required more horses, fewer workers were needed. A good header operation could harvest 40 acres (16 hectares) in a long, hot day.

Daniel Best's idea was to combine the header with his portable cleaning machine. All that was then needed was to add a threshing mechanism. This resulted in what Best called his Traveling Combined Harvester. By fall 1885, he sold six of these machines, the forerunners of what would become known as the "combine."

Daniel Best had done well in California and was established in business and in his community. On August 24, 1890, the *Pacific Rural Press* praised his contributions to the opening of the American West: "Mr. Best is a genial, modest and reliable citizen, prosperous in business and enjoying a reputation as a man of veracity and integrity. He has been blessed in domestic relations, and his hospitable home is surrounded by a most estimable wife and six promising children."

The Holt Brothers Come West

In 1864, another young man by the name of Charles Holt made his way to California. He sailed by steamship from New York, around Cape Horn, to San Francisco, where he had been promised a job. Upon his arrival, though, he found that his would-be employer had gone bankrupt. With typical New England pluck, Holt went to work as a schoolteacher and kept books for a general merchandise store in the evenings.

Holt stemmed from a New Hampshire family long established in the hardwood lumber and carriage businesses. Seeing a burgeoning need for horse-drawn conveyances in prosperous Northern California, in 1869 Holt established C. H. Holt & Company of Beale Street, San Francisco.

Holt began importing hardwood carriage components from his family's business back East. The lumber was cut in Ohio, shipped to New Hampshire for seasoning, then fashioned into axles, tongues, and wheels before being shipped around the Horn to Holt, where his company constructed the carriages. By 1871, Charles's three brothers had joined him, and the firm was renamed Holt Brothers.

The hot, dry California climate created problems for

Holt Caterpillar Combined Harvester, 1916
This Combined Harvester was on display at the Kansas State Fair in Hutchinson, Kansas, in 1916. Standing at the steering wheel is Robert Patterson Brebner. A native of Scotland, Brebner came in 1910 to the United States as an engineer and went to work for Holt demonstrating gas-engined harvesters. With the advent of World War I, Brebner enlisted in the U.S. Army and served with General John "Black Jack" Pershing's expedition into Mexico in search of revolutionary Pancho Villa; Brebner was responsible for keeping the Holt crawlers running and for training drivers. In 1918, he was mustered out of the army and went back to Holt. Brebner eventually owned a Caterpillar dealership in Green Bay, Wisconsin.

the Holt's wares, however. Wheels made of the Eastern wood dried out in the Western weather, causing spokes to shrink and rims to fall off. To combat the problem, the company moved in 1883 to Stockton, California, an area of extremely low humidity. Here, the lumber was given a full seasoning before it was made into wheels, which corrected the problem.

With the move in 1883, the firm's name was changed to the Stockton Wheel Company. The youngest brother, Benjamin, was made president and the eldest brother, William, stayed in San Francisco to handle imports. Brother Frank returned to run the New Hampshire part of the business, while Charles and Benjamin, along with William's son, Pliny, moved to Stockton.

The hardwood imports netted the Holt company a dramatic 300 percent profit. The Holts were paid for their products in gold, which they then shipped back East where it was converted into paper money, doubling its value. Controlling all levels of production, the Holts made tremendous profits on their imports. With ample cash for expanding and experimenting with new products, it was little surprise that their woodworking talents soon turned to creating their own version of the combined harvester made famous by Daniel Best.

The Golden Land of California

Prior to the discovery of gold in 1849, less than 15,000 settlers of European descent inhabited California. By 1860, the number had swollen to some 400,000. When the gold rush waned, many people stayed on in the golden land, finding work and making their fortunes in logging, farming, and other burgeoning businesses. The need for food soon outstripped supply as locally grown food production could not keep up with the rapid increase in popula-

Daniel Best steamer and harvester, circa 1905
A postcard promoted the Golden State's bountiful wheatfields with this scene of a Best harvesting team in San Joaquin County near Stockton.

Logging with horse power, 1890s
Logging before the creation of the Holt and Best steamers was powered by horse teams. Here, ten horses and a Big Wheel haul a mammoth log. (Eastman Collection, University of California–Davis)

Daniel Best steam traction engine, circa 1905
Best and Holt's steamers burst onto the logging scene in the Pacific Northwest in the 1890s, revolutionizing the industry. In creating his steamer, Best bought the rights to the Remington steam engine, improved on the design, and went into production in 1889. The Remington was designed for use in the woods; the Best engines were suitable for logging as well as for farm use. (Eastman Collection, University of California–Davis)

tion. Newcomers from the East and Midwest who attempted to farm were dismayed at the growing conditions. The summers were long, dry, and incredibly hot. The soil had no sod, since the grasses died out in the heat. When horses and wagons traversed the California plains, the soil turned to hub-deep dust. That dust choked the horses and drivers and ruined the wheel bearings.

If necessity is the mother of invention, then high price is the father. When the cost of a 100-pound bag of flour rose to $100, new methods of planting were tried. Farmers discovered that if they plowed and planted in the fall rainy season, the otherwise barren land could yield great wheat harvests. By 1890, California was the number two wheat-producing state in the nation.

Northern California's Central and San Joaquin Valleys proved ideal for mechanized wheat farming. Level, fertile soil produced wheat yields of two and even three times as many bushels per acre as those back East. The hot, dry conditions allowed the use of the early crude combines, while farmers in the Midwest and most of the Great Plains were forced to stick with the binder-harvester and threshing machine for another fifty or sixty years.

Besides the vast, level wheatfields of the Central Valley, some of the best farmland was in the Sacramento River Delta. A half million acres (200,000 hectares) were drained by the delta, and the soil was extremely rich with peat created by the decomposition of tule plants and alluvial deposits. This delta was largely unexploited because of the spongy soil, but a series of drainage ditches was eventually made. To work the soil, horses were shod with "tule shoes," which were similar to snowshoes, being one foot or more in diameter and made of a stout mesh; they were tied to each hoof to spread the horses' weight over the soft earth. With the tule shoes, the teams could pull wagons and other implements with extra-wide wheel rims.

Great farms developed in the San Joaquin Valley near Stockton. Wheat ranches of 40,000 or more acres (16,000+ hectares) were created. One ranch had a field seventeen miles (27 km) long; plowers and harvesters camped at the far end at night and returned the next day. Vast numbers of draft animals were required: one large ranch reportedly had more than 1,000 horses and mules. By the 1870s, threshing was done by threshing machines powered by four or five teams walking in a circle. Larger ranches had stationary steam engines. Transportation was mostly by riverboat or giant wagon trains; some wagons were pulled by as many as forty mules. Rail transport was coming on strong.

By the dawn of the 1900s, California—and especially the area inland from San Francisco—was one of the most prosperous areas in the world, thanks to mining and agriculture as well as the support businesses that grew up with them. The city of Stockton became a center of implement manufacturing, and many of the implements were designed specifically for use in the area's conditions.

Best and Holt Go Head to Head

By late 1883, the Holt brothers' Stockton Wheel Company manufactured wagon wheels, freight wagons, harnesses, wagon hardware, and mining equipment. Charles and Benjamin bought out the interests of their two brothers shortly after the company arrived in Stockton; Charles ran the financial side of the business while Benjamin handled manufacturing and development.

Ben Holt was quick to see the labor-saving potential of what he called the "Traveling Thrasher." Two years after moving to Stockton, the Holts expanded into the combine business, buying several promising patents and building new manufacturing facilities. Daniel Best sold his first combine in 1885, and the Holts followed fast on his heels, selling their first machine in 1886.

The first Holt combine boasted a 14-foot (420-cm) header and a 21-inch (52.50-cm) threshing cylinder. The mechanism was driven by power transmitted via a link-belt chain from the unit's wheels. Other combine makers used gears to convey the power from the wheels, which caused them two problems. First, the gears wore rapidly in the dusty conditions. Second, gear-driven threshing mechanisms could be ruined when horse teams bolted. To operate the monstrous combines, teams of twenty-five to thirty horses were employed; controlling such a menagerie was often a superhuman task. Horses were easily spooked by hornet nests, snakes, flushed quail, or sharp noises, panicking the team into a run-away. During a run-away, horses and drivers were often injured or killed, and the threshing mechanisms were often overspeeded and driven to destruction.

Ben Holt's chain-driven power transmission system solved both the problems of gear wear and overspeeding during run-aways. Holt's link-belt drive was quieter and more efficient than the gear system used on Best's and others' machines. If a run-away occurred, the Holt combine's chain would break, preventing damage to the drive and threshing mechanism. The chain could be repaired by simply replacing the link that failed. The chain drive soon made the Holt combine famous and won it 90 percent of the West Coast trade.

In 1891, Holt introduced a self-leveling combine that made it possible to work on hillsides. This feature, as much as the chain drive, accounted for the Holt machine's popularity. And, in 1892, the firm's name changed again, this time to the Holt Manufacturing Company.

Daniel Best was not sitting on his hands, however. An inveterate inventor, he now had several patents unrelated

Above: Holt steamer, circa 1900

Dwarfed by the size of the machine, lumberjacks at a logging camp in the Pacific Northwest proudly pose with their Holt steamer. (Eastman Collection, University of California–Davis)

Left: Daniel Best advertisement, 1889

"Plowing and Harvesting by Steam a Success," this magazine ad proudly announced. "I am now manufacturing the Celebrated Remington Traction Engine or Steam Plow, adapted to all kinds of heavy work usually done by mules or horses. A number of these Engines are now in use, giving entire satisfaction, for plowing and pulling Combined Harvesters. I have also patented and put into the field a successful Steam Harvester, which the above cut represents. . . ."

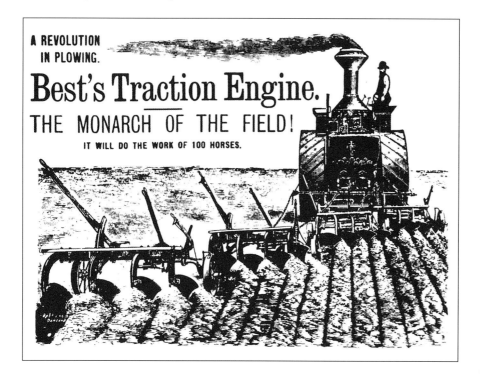

Daniel Best advertisement, 1890s
"A Revolution in Plowing," promised this ad. Labeling its machines "The Monarch of the Field," Daniel Best stated that his steamers "will do the work of 100 horses."

Holt steamer, circa 1900
A Holt steamer hauls a train of six wagons laden with cut boards from a sawmill in the Pacific Northwest. (Eastman Collection, University of California–Davis)

Best pulling Holt pulling log wagons, 1902
Disproving the notion that Daniel Best and Benjamin Holt did not cooperate, Best and Holt steamers jointly pull a train of four log wagons. (Eastman Collection, University of California–Davis)

to harvesters, including one for a clothes-washing machine. He took on business partners in both Oregon and Oakland, California. In Oakland, his fast-growing cleaner and harvester manufacturing operations spilled out into the streets around the factory, and complaints from the police prompted Best to move to larger quarters. In late 1886, he purchased the San Leandro Plow Company, consolidated his operations, and moved everything to San Leandro, California.

The Best combine's claim to fame hinged not on the drive mechanism, but on a fan-governor. In the event of a bolting team, the dramatically increased fan speed absorbed so much power that the drive wheel slipped and the threshing mechanism could not overspeed. Since Holt's combines outsold those of Daniel Best, one might assume they were superior. Still, more than 150 Best combines were at work by 1890.

It was at this time that Daniel Best's attention was diverted from the combine war with the Holts. In 1890, a large steam engine came rumbling into San Leandro after a 600-mile (960-km) trip from Oregon. It pulled to a stop in front of the Daniel Best Agricultural Works.

The First Steamers

When the temperature of water is raised to 212 degrees Fahrenheit (100° Celsius), it expands to 1,600 times its original volume. If the vapor is confined, pressure increases rapidly; further heat causes the pressure to increase even more. Harnessing this water vapor pressure is the fundamental goal of the steam engine.

The first steam "engine" is credited to an Egyptian inventor named Hero. About 120 B.C., Hero mounted a hollow globe on a pipe connected to a steam kettle. On opposite sides of the globe, he mounted L-shaped pipes. With a fire burning under the kettle, steam rushed through the pipe, into the globe, and out of the L-shaped pipes causing the globe to rotate. Still, it would be some 1,600 years before there was practical application of Hero's discovery.

Due to metallurgical limitations of the day, early steam engines of the 1800s were so heavy that uses were restricted to stationary applications and ships; sometime later, steam technology was adapted to railroads. In the mid-1800s,

the perfection of the Bessemer steel-making process made lightweight but powerful steam engines possible. First came the portable engine, which could be towed to a location and used to power machinery. Next, drive wheels were added, but the device still required a hitch of horses to steer the front axle. Finally, the self-propelled steam traction engine was created, with an engineer in the cab to guide and control the machine.

One of the pioneer steam traction engine makers in the Western states was DeLafayette Remington of Woodburn, Oregon. A Remington engine was probably the first to be operated in the woods to skid logs, as it had several features that were especially useful to lumberjacks. First, it had a single front wheel with steam-powered steering, which made it considerably more maneuverable than steamers with two wide-set front wheels. Second, it boasted a vertical boiler rather than the more conventional horizontal boiler common to railroad locomotives. Set aft between the two eight-foot-diameter (240-cm) drive wheels, the vertical boiler was not subjected to as much twisting and jostling stress as a horizontal boiler when operating on uneven ground.

Remington had met Daniel Best when Best was in the lumbering business in Oregon. When Remington's engine factory in Woodburn burned down, he decided to sell his engine patents and leave the business. This inspired Remington to drive his remaining steam traction engine all of the way to San Leandro. Proving perhaps for the first time the adage that working hardware makes the best engineering proposal, Best bought the rights to the Remington engine on the spot.

The Remington engine was quickly improved and upgraded by Best. Within a short time, substantial numbers of the steamers went to work in logging and farming.

Best also immediately integrated the steam engine with the combine. The steamer provided motivating power, and, via a flexible pipe, provided steam for a separate motor that drove the cutting, threshing, and cleaning mechanisms. The first Best engine paired with the first Best steam-powered combine was delivered in 1889.

By 1890, only three West Coast harvester companies remained: the Holts' Stockton Wheel Company, Daniel Best Agricultural Works, and Stockton Combined Harvester and Agricultural Works, a conglomeration of several combine makers. But with his jump to the steam harvester, Best garnered the majority of the market.

Not to be outdone, Holt responded by developing a steamer of his own. His first engine was sold in 1890, and featured link-belt drive instead of gears. Holt soon also integrated his steam engine with his combine. Thereafter, the Best factory concentrated on steam engines while Holt vigorously pursued the production of combines, outproducing Best eight to one in that field.

BEST

1913 Daniel Best logo

Above: Caterpillar R4 and Holt Combine, 1930s
This Holt Combine was still cutting grain in California in the 1930s, solid proof of the quality of the design.

Right: Daniel Best steamer ghost
An abandoned Best round-wheel steam traction engine put out to pasture after years of hard labor. (Eastman Collection, University of California–Davis)

CHAPTER 2

"She Crawls Along Like a Caterpillar"

The Development of Gas Tractors and Crawlers, 1890–1915

Above: Benjamin Holt and Holt Model 40, 1908
Ben Holt examines the first Holt gas-powered crawler used for farming. (Smithsonian Institution)

Left: 1913 Holt Model 60
This Model 60 was purchased new for $4,205 by the Hahn brothers, who ran a ranch in Colusa, California. It was used on the ranch until sold at an estate sale in 1980. Owners: Larry Maasdam and Ron Miller.

Although Holt focused on combine construction, the proximity of his Stockton works to the Mormon Slough bog land of the Sacramento River Delta inspired a new market for the firm. To work the wet soil, Benjamin Holt adapted tracks to his steam engines in place of wheels.

At the dawn of the 1900s, the use of tracks to spread a machine's weight over a larger area and reduce its footprint pressure was not a new idea. As early as 1825, Englishman George Cayley patented an endless chain-belt track system to support wagons traveling over soft ground. A few years later, this arrangement was applied to the steam Heathcoate Plowing Engine in England.

In 1858, in Marysville, California—three years later to become the home of Henry and Zechariah Best—a successful tracked steam traction engine was demonstrated by inventor Warren Miller. Apparently Miller built only one such machine, however. Other tracked steamers followed in North America, including those built by Minnis in 1869, Parvin in 1871, and Stratton in 1893. The most successful and widely produced steam crawler was Alvin O. Lombard's Lombard Log Hauler, which made its debut in 1900. The Lombard was built by the Waterville Iron Works in Penobscot County, Maine, and under license by the Phoenix Company in Eau Claire, Wisconsin. Benjamin Holt and his nephews Pliny and Ben C. Holt traveled the United States and abroad to review the state of tracked steam engine development.

Birth of the Caterpillar Tractor

To build his new track-type tractor, Benjamin Holt adapted tracks to one of his successful wheel machines. Holt's experience with the link-belt drive system took the metallurgical mysteries out of developing tracks for the firm's own steamer: Holt simply bolted wooden blocks to two link chains to make each track for his first tracked steamer. He retained the single front steering wheel, but

CATERPILLAR

CATERPILLAR

CATERPILLAR

Caterpillar logos
Early development of Holt's Caterpillar logo through the 1910s.

devised clutches for each track to further facilitate turning. Brakes were not provided, but by declutching the track on the inside of a turn, the front wheel would bring the 40,000-pound (18,000-kg) monster around, aided by the thrust of the outside track.

The tracked Holt was first tested in November 1904 on tule land outside of Stockton. As the giant machine clippity-clopped back to the factory after the successful test, a spectator commented to Benjamin Holt, "She crawls along like a caterpillar." Holt reportedly replied, "'Caterpillar' she is!" He later registered the name as his trademark. The name would soon become one of the world's most famous trademarks.

The Dawn of the Internal-Combustion Engine

While steam power had been growing in acceptance throughout the 1800s, near the end of the nineteenth century a new type of engine was developed. In 1876, German inventor Nikolaus August Otto created a practical four-cycle internal-combustion engine that was fueled by a waste byproduct known as gasoline. Even then, the invention was recognized as being so important that the courts of Europe ordered the patents into the public domain. Motoring pioneers by the names of Gottlieb Daimler, the brothers Duryea, Ransom Olds, and Henry Ford brought the Otto-cycle engine into the twentieth century.

The first Otto-engined tractor to perform useful commercial work as well as propel itself backwards and forwards was the 1892 Froelich machine, crafted by Iowa engineer John Froelich. It was little more than a Van Duzen one-cylinder engine mounted on steam-engine running gear. It did prove the concept, however, and eliminated the problems of boiler explosions, fires, and the insatiable thirst for water associated with steam engines.

Daniel Best began experimenting with Otto-cycle engines as early as 1891. His first large gasoline-fueled engine drove a generator to produce electricity, providing power to run his factory. Soon his gas engines were powering various vehicles including streetcars and automobiles—as well as an automobile of his own design.

By mid-1893, the first Otto-engined tractor emerged from the Best factory. It was a conversion of a Best steamer, now powered by a four-cylinder engine. The tractor had the unique feature of a clutch between cylinders two and three; for light duty, the machine could be run on only two cylinders.

The Holts also recognized the potential of the Otto engine. Benjamin reportedly bought one of the first automobiles to be seen in Stockton, a 1903 Oldsmobile. In 1905, he built a three-wheeled vehicle of his own for use around the plant.

Minnis Steam Crawler, circa 1869
Developed in Ames, Iowa, the Minnis machine had a tricycle arrangement of three tracks. Steam cylinders powered the rear two. Apparently, only one Minnis crawler was built.

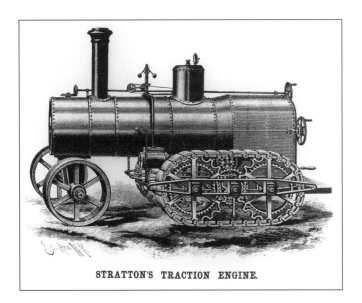

STRATTON'S TRACTION ENGINE.

Stratton Traction Crawler, 1893
The Stratton Crawler was made in Moscow, Pennsylvania. The steering mechanism appears to have been quite light-duty for the job. Notice the curious windlass attached to the front of the tracks.

Holt steam crawler, 1908
Only a few of these 50-hp steamers were built before Holt switched to gasoline engines. This version had steam-powered steering.

Benjamin and Pliny Holt formed the Aurora Engine Company in 1906, in order to develop gas engines without upsetting Holt stockholders who favored the tried-and-true technology of steam. Headquarters of the new company were on Stockton's Aurora Street, and although separate from the Holt Manufacturing Company, its operations were well integrated. By 1908, Caterpillar tractors with Aurora engines were rolling out of the Holt factory, and there were more than a hundred Holt gasoline tractors in service by 1910. In addition, Holt had more problem-solving service men traveling the roads of California than they had salesmen. Aurora gas engines were applied to Holt combines, replacing the steam power of the past. Aurora also made some experimental tractors.

1920 Holt logo

Caterpillar Collector Profile:
Larry Maasdam

Larry Maasdam and his wife Melanie reside about two miles north of Clarion, a pleasant community in north-central Iowa. Their home is on the sprawling grounds of Maasdam's drainage ditch construction company, an operation employing modern Caterpillar and other equipment, founded in 1953 with a single D6.

Although raised on an Iowa farm, Maasdam came by his interest in ditching honestly. Maasdam's father invented a ditching machine, at first for his own use, but then sold the rights to what is now known as the Vermeer Trencher. Maasdam went out on his own with the D6 when he was just eighteen years old.

Like many others who make their living with machines, Maasdam has a hard time getting rid of a faithful Caterpillar when its economic life has expired. In fact, he still owns the 1953 D6 "Hard-Nose" bulldozer that he started the business with. Besides this type of more-or-less natural antique collecting, Maasdam has also purchased many rare and unusual Caterpillar and Holt items. Along with some of the employees of the company, Maasdam's son Ryan helped with the restorations.

Besides the home place, Maasdam keeps his growing collection in several locations in the town of Clarion, and at the Jenison-Meacham Memorial Art Center and Museum in Belmond, Iowa. The center is the show grounds for the local farm antiques collectors club. In one of the big sheds at the center, Maasdam keeps his 1917 Holt 24-foot hillside combine. This machine is self-propelled by a Holt 6.00x7.00-inch (150x175-mm) bore-and-stroke, 45-hp, four-cylinder engine.

Besides the Holt and Caterpillar pieces shown on these pages, the Maasdam collection includes a huge Minneapolis 22/44, several Averys, a large assortment of various brands of high-crop wheel tractors, a rare Massey-Harris 44 Vineyard, and Melanie Maasdam's own John Deere 520 LPG. In another display area, walls are lined with lighted shelves containing thousands of scale models and toys of every scale and description. Most are highly detailed collectors items; some are one-of-a-kind hand-built models. The collection also includes porcelain signs and a variety of dealer clocks.

Above: 1913 Holt Model 60
Turns were made by releasing one steering clutch and pivoting the front tiller wheel. No steering brakes were provided, so only wide, sweeping turns could be accomplished. A considerable amount of human effort went into controlling one of these monsters.

Left: 1913 Holt Model 60
The 1,230-ci (20,147-cc), four-cylinder, overhead-valve engine was rated at 50 drawbar and 60 belt hp at 500 rpm.

Facing page: 1913 Holt Model 60
Larry Maasdam drives the Model 60, serial number 1838.

THE HOLT MFG. CO. STOCKTON CAL.

Above: 1913 Holt Model 60

The 60 came equipped with a special oil can to lubricate the tracks and a hand pump to pressurize the fuel tank.

Left: 1913 Holt Model 60

Tom and Doug Dauterman restored this machine over a fifteen-month period, putting in more than 1,900 hours of work.

Holt Baby Caterpillar advertisement, 1913

The Baby Caterpillar developed 20 drawbar and 30 brake hp. As this ad sternly noted, "The creeping motion of the track suggested the name 'Caterpillar.' We protected it as our trade-mark. It is ours, and ours alone. There is no other Caterpillar but the Holt."

Holt-powered artillery regiment, 1917
Thirty 45-hp Holt Caterpillars comprised the first motorized artillery regiment in the U.S. Army, the Ninth Field Artillery, stationed at Schofield Barracks in Hawaii. (National Archives)

1921 Holt Model 75

The 75 was powered by a 1,400-ci (22,932-cc), four-cylinder engine and two-speed transmission. Bore and stroke was 7.50x8.00 inches (187.50x200 mm), giving 50 drawbar and 75 belt hp at 550 rpm. A K-W magneto provided spark. Owner: Larry Maasdam.

Above: Holt Model 75, circa 1920
Production of the Model 75 began in Stockton in 1913 and in Peoria in 1914; it ended in 1924. (Smithsonian Institution)

Right: 1917 Holt Caterpillar advertisement

It's Construction That *Insures Lasting* "Caterpillar" Tractor Service

Expert knowledge of materials, coupled with thirty-five years of experience in farm machinery designing and building, has enabled Holt Engineers to make the "Caterpillar" Tractor a machine of exceptional service and efficiency.

It is that knowledge which has taught them to make certain parts of the "Caterpillar" Tractor steel, certain parts of special alloys, some surfaces chilled and some surfaces case-hardened.

Expert knowledge and choice of materials and solid construction insure lasting service—a feature of this tractor that puts bigger profits into the hands of "Caterpillar" Tractor owners. The experience of the thousands of satisfied "Caterpillar" Tractor owners is a safe guide for you to follow.

We will gladly send full "Caterpillar" Tractor information on request.

CATERPILLAR
Reg. U.S. Pat. Off.

The Holt
MANUFACTURING CO. Inc.
Stockton, Cal.   Peoria, Ill.
Los Angeles, Cal.
Portland, Ore.
Spokane, Wash.
San Francisco, Cal.

Above: 1921 Holt Model 75
Besides the front tiller wheel, steering clutches and brakes were provided on the Model 75. The large wheels at the rear are the clutches for the tracks.

Left: 1921 Holt Model 75
A variety of different fan and radiator configurations were used on the Holt 75. The machine weighed about 23,000 pounds (10,350 kg).

Left, top: Fowler Gyrotiller, 1930

The British Fowler Gyrotiller was based on Holt running gear and developed by Holt engineer Robert Brebner and Briton Norman Storey. Storey came to Holt for help in developing a crawler-tiller following World War I. Holt declined to help, but Brebner left Holt and went with Storey to Puerto Rico, where they developed the Gyrotiller from Holt parts. C. H. Fowler, head of the Fowler Company, was in the market to replace his fading steam engine business, and while vacationing in Puerto Rico, he saw a Gyrotiller at work and bought the manufacturing rights on the spot from Storey. The Gyrotiller found acceptance only in sugar cane country, however.

Left, bottom: 1921 Holt Model 75 and 1913 Holt Model 60

The holes in the flywheel were for a crowbar starter. This starting method seems terribly difficult and dangerous to the uninitiated, but actually works quite well as long as everything is up to snuff. An engine backfire, however, can throw the bar a considerable distance.

Holt Caterpillar advertisement, 1918
As this ad proudly stated, "The 'Caterpillar' Tractor was invented by Benjamin Holt for the American farmer. In the farmer's hands it made good. Then industrial users all over the world proved it the most economical solution of their difficult power problems. . . ."

1921 Holt Model 75
The first time owner Larry Maasdam tried plowing with his 75, it had trouble pulling a ten-bottom plow. Later, he discovered he had been operating it in high gear. He tried it again in low, and it pulled the ten bottoms so easily that the governor was hardly opening.

Moving house with a crawler, 1910s
A powerful crawler was the ideal house mover. (Glenbow Archives)

CHAPTER 3

Joining Forces

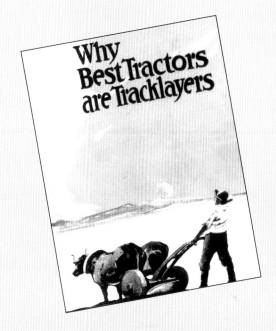

The Acquisition of Best by Holt—and the Rise of C. L. Best, 1905–1924

Above: 1920s C. L. Best brochure

Left: 1925 C. L. Best Thirty Orchard
Owner Jerry Gast aboard his Thirty Orchard, serial number S3279.

By the dawn of the 1900s, Best and Holt tractors were being widely used in farming, logging, and construction on the West Coast. Their tractors competed in plowing and pulling contests, although these were not always fair competitions, since modifications to the standard production machines were the norm. Both manufacturers continued to make combine harvesters for the world trade as well. Best soon introduced its own version of the hillside harvester, as created by Holt.

The intense competition between the two West Coast manufacturers inevitably led to patent infringement litigation. In 1905, Best sued Holt for usurping its patents on the steam-powered auxiliary motor used to power the combine cutting and threshing mechanisms. Legal wrangling went on for three long years.

In the end, a surprising conclusion was reached: In 1908, Daniel Best sold his Daniel Best Agricultural Works to the Holt Manufacturing Company for a reported $325,000. Daniel Best was then seventy years old; he was tired of the never-ending legal hassles with Holt and was ready to retire. The deal included an arrangement whereby Best's son, C. L. "Leo" Best, was to buy one-third of the stock in the Holt firm before the sale. This would have given C. L. Best a substantial interest in the combined corporation, which retained the name Holt Manufacturing Company. The Holts would have majority control.

TRACKLAYER

About Our President

Mr. C. L. Best was reared in the tractor manufacturing business. His first experience was in the manufacture of round-wheel steam tractors and combined harvesters, long before the advent of the gas engine. In fact, the first successful steam farm tractor built in California was constructed by the Best Company, and placed on board cars in San Leandro, February 8, 1889.

Shortly over a decade ago, Mr. Best founded the C. L. Best Gas Traction Company. The plant now covers eight acres of land, and Best Tracklayer Tractors are in successful operation in nearly every country on the globe. Design and construction are based upon years of operation of Best Tractors in the field.

Mr. Best believes in concentration. As a result there is one product of the Best factory—Best Tracklayer Tractors. Concentration has always kept Best Tractors dominant. Concentration made it possible for Best to step out in the lead of other tractor manufacturers ten years ago, when in-closed steel cut gears running in oil were installed. A little later the pace was again set by the construction of the all-steel tracklayer.

The "25" and the "60" now stand as crowning achievements as the result of these years of practical manufacturing combined with Yankee ingenuity expressed in design, materials and construction. The aim has always been to build for maximum results for the user of the Best Tractor. The Best organization has always given first consideration to a quality product. Assuredly Best Tracklayer Tractors are quality tractors. There can be no challenge to the statement that Mr. C. L. Best is one of the foremost tractor engineers in the world.

C. L. Best, President and Founder of the C. L. Best Gas Traction Co.

BEST Tracklayer Tractors [Page twenty-three]

C. L. Best chafed under the arrangement and never paid for his stock. He worked with Holt for less than two years, and then left the company. With financial help from his father, he created in 1910 the C. L. Best Gas Traction Engine Company of Elmhurst, California. He established a steel-casting plant near his factory to make engine blocks and other tractor parts, and was soon producing a full line of wheeled tractors ranging in size from 20 to 80 hp.

Holt Expands to the East

During the same time period, the growing sales of both crawler tractors and combines led the Holt Manufacturing Company to consider expanding east. The vast prairies of the Great Plains were being planted with Red Fife and Turkey Red wheat strains imported from the steppes of Russia; these varieties had short stems and hard kernels that made them ideal for the American Midwest. Large wheat farms were being developed from the Canadian prairies to Kansas and Oklahoma and all the way to the Rocky Mountains. The time seemed ripe for expansion, so Benjamin Holt dispatched Pliny Holt to seek a new manufacturing site for crawler tractors to cover this burgeoning market. As part of their plan, combines would initially be shipped east from Stockton.

Pliny Holt chose Minneapolis, a booming metropolis on the Mississippi River that was then the world's largest center for flour milling. He had received his engineering training there at the University of Minnesota. He acquired factory space with the Diamond Iron Works and hired a staff. Early in 1909, crawler components were shipped from Stockton and assembly of Caterpillar tractors began. The Eastern outfit was formed as a separate firm called the Northern Holt Company with Pliny Holt as president. A Canadian branch was added to Northern Holt shortly thereafter.

The first two Minneapolis-built Caterpillar tractors were sold by the end of 1909, bringing in around $7,000. It was not a bad start for Northern Holt—except that expenses for the year ran to $12,000! As the year progressed, Pliny Holt wrote to Uncle Ben asking for further capitalization, stating that all other avenues of raising working cash had been exhausted. Ben's response indicated that neither Holt Manufacturing, nor he himself had funds to lend: Things were tough all over. For a while, it seemed that the eastern expansion might be a bust.

The activities of Pliny Holt and his associates did not go unnoticed, however. A Peoria, Illinois, implement dealer named Murray M. Baker sent word to Pliny Holt

C. L. Best, circa 1920s
A rare photograph of "Leo" Best from a 1920s brochure, which noted that he "was reared in the tractor manufacturing business."

1920 C. L. Best Sixty
This 1920 Sixty is all original from its tracks to its low-hours engine—only the radiator has been repainted. The original owner had worked for C. L. Best and acquired this tractor from the factory when he started farming in Hanford, California. The tractor was used on the farm until 1951. Owner: Ed Claessen.

of the availability of the recently defunct Colean Manu-facturing Company's facilities in East Peoria, Illinois. Colean had been one of the many steam tractor makers that failed to make the switch to gas engines. The failure of Colean had hurt the Peoria area, and local financiers were anxious to get the factory going again. Favorable terms were offered, with Baker acting as a go-between. He even put in his own money to prevent the sale of the factory to others. Thus, for $75,000—and only $11,500 down—a factory worth $250,000 was obtained by North-ern Holt. And not only was a fully functional workspace acquired, but having such an asset on the books also helped obtain further financing. Baker had impressed the Holts with his aggressive and optimistic spirit, and so he became the vice president and general manager of the Peo-ria operation, established in January 1910 as the Holt Cat-erpillar Company.

Hard Times in the Tractor Business

By 1910, the two old rivals, Holt and Best, were again in strong competition. Holt was considerably larger, but Best had good products in its wheel-type machines, and was ahead in the development of gas engines. C. L. Best's firm was small, but well financed due to Daniel Best's resources. Holt now boasted some 800 employees, but it was over-extended financially because of the Minneapolis expan-sion.

Holt also suffered from a duplication of effort, due to the independence of the Holt and Aurora Engine Com-panies in Stockton, Holt Caterpillar Company in Peoria, and several other Holt-owned entities. Meanwhile, Holt was making every effort to expand sales overseas. C. Parker Holt had made a sales trip to Argentina with great success while Benjamin went on an extended marketing tour of Europe and Russia. When he returned from this trip, how-ever, Benjamin Holt found that Aurora had more than 400 overstocked engines gathering dust. At this point, he determined to consolidate his empire.

Charles L. Neumiller, longtime lawyer for Holt, finally convinced the heads of the eight companies under the Holt banner that they would all benefit by merging into one gigantic corporation. On December 31, 1912, this dramatic reorganization helped the new Holt Manufac-turing Company raise the necessary financing to put it on sound footing for the next decade.

Looming legal battles would consume much of both

companies' energy over the next decade, however. C. L. Best had made several wheeled tractors, but in 1912 he came out with a 75-hp crawler that was much the same as the current Holt machine. To add insult to injury, Best audaciously used the name "Caterpillar" in his advertising. Naturally, Holt sued for patent and trademark infringement, and a tempestuous legal battle followed.

Best was crafty, however. He quickly acquired two key patents owned by inventor Alvin Lombard for his famous tracked Lombard Log Hauler—patents which predated Holt's own crawler patent. With the Lombard patents, Best prevailed in the lawsuit, although the court ruled that he could not use the term "Caterpillar" in the future. Denied the use of this term, Best adopted the trademark "Tracklayer."

Best then sublicensed the old Lombard patent rights to Holt for seed money that helped him place the C. L. Best Gas Traction Engine Company on firm feet. Best, of course, also retained the rights to build his own crawlers. In turn, Holt was able to exact royalties from other crawler makers, including the Monarch Tractor Company of Springfield, Illinois; Cleveland Motor Plow Company of Cleveland, Ohio; and Bates Machine & Tractor Company

of Joliet, Illinois, builder of the aptly named Bates Steel Mule. These royalties helped Holt recoup its losses.

New Models for New Times

C. L. Best had copied the Holt machine in designing his Model 75, but he also added many refinements. Best incorporated numerous improvements in metallurgy into his 75, thanks to the blossoming automobile business, which was spawning dramatic advances such as the novel vanadium steel alloy, the metal that made the Model T Ford possible.

Other differences between the Holt and Best machines included an improved track oscillation feature on the Best 75, reducing stresses in the main frame. The Best machine also used a differential gear set to drive the two tracks; Holt tractor drivers were forced to declutch the inside track for turns. Both methods had advantages and disadvantages. The Best Tracklayer would out pull the Holt Caterpillar on a turn—that is, until one track lost traction. Then, the Holt would continue to pull; however, an alternating straight-curve-straight-curve path would have to be followed.

Best painted his tractors black with gold letters

1916 C. L. Best crawler patent drawing
In 1913, C. L. Best applied for a patent for his crawler-style tractor. The patent was eventually granted in 1916.

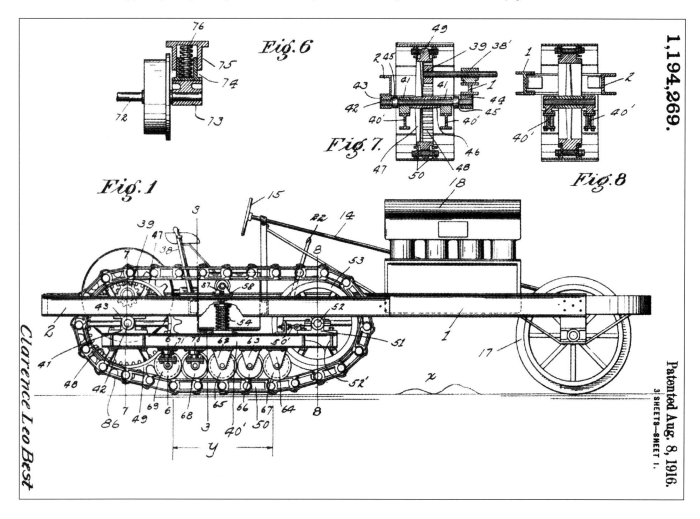

whereas Holt's were brown with yellow trim. From a distance it was difficult to tell them apart and in black-and-white photographs it was even harder to differentiate them—which helped Best, who reportedly used pictures of Holt machines in his own advertisements.

In 1915, Best introduced two smaller tractors, the 30-hp Muley and the 16-hp Pony. These were unique in that they did not use the tiller front wheel. Instead, turning brakes controlled the track speeds to make turns.

Prosperity had come to the C. L. Best Gas Traction Company. The Model 75 provided most of the income, but the Muley, Pony, and other smaller models contributed their share. The fledgling business had outgrown its Elmhurst factory and more manufacturing space was needed. In mid-1916, C. L. Best was able to repurchase and transfer operations to the old San Leandro plant that his father had built up years ago. In late 1920, the firm's name was changed in time with the modern era of tractor technology to the C. L. Best Gas Tractor Company.

Holt also introduced models that were both smaller and larger than its standard 75. With orders rolling in from more than forty countries, prosperity had come to all plants. The Caterpillar Model 45 was the first from Peoria. It was unique in that it had a two-wheel wide front. Stockton produced a smaller Model 18 in 1912 designed especially for orchard use. It was also the first Caterpillar tractor to dispense with the tiller wheel. In 1914, a Peoria version called the Baby Caterpillar made its debut; an improved version in 1915 was named the Caterpillar Junior. The largest Caterpillar tractor of the 1910s was the giant 70/120. It weighed more than 12 tons (10,800 kg) and boasted a drawbar pull of 12,600 pounds (5,670 kg). Holt also introduced several other medium and small tractors.

Big Iron and the Big War

Around 1910, a Hungarian farmer named Leo Steiner read reports of the large-scale mechanized farms in North America. Steiner was the owner of a huge agricultural estate, and because much of his farm had wet soil, he opted to order a Holt Caterpillar Model 60. He used the

Caterpillar Collector Profile: Jerry Gast

Wapello, Iowa, is the home of Jerry and Linda Gast and Gast's large machine shop business. Their son Clayton and his wife Ruby reside in the neighboring town of Grandview, where the growing Caterpillar collection is.

As a kid, Gast grew up around a neighbor's Holt 75. Gast's father also had several bulldozers around the place, and he says he grew up with a soft spot for crawlers.

Gast had two years of engineering school in junior college and then went into a four-year apprentice machinist course at the Rock Island Arsenal, graduating in 1967. From there, he went directly into his own business.

Starting and operating a business can be a stressful undertaking, so when a neighbor offered an F-20 Farmall at a reasonable price for restoration, Gast jumped at it. Working on the Farmall in the evening became good therapy. More Farmalls followed, and then one of Gast's employees told him of a "distressed" Caterpillar Thirty in a hog yard not far away. After that project, wheeled tractors were child's play, and Gast has been accepting the challenge of Best and Caterpillar restorations since.

There are now ten Cats on the place, two Cat pull graders and an Adams, the original fleet of Farmalls, and a variety of parts tractors. As an interesting aside, world-class Oliver collector-restorer Gary Spitznogle lives across the road from the Gasts.

Two versions of the 1920s Best Tracklayer logo

1920 C. L. Best Sixty
Although called the Sixty to denote a power rating of 60 hp, University of Nebraska tests in 1921 achieved only 55 hp at 656 rpm—even with the air cleaner removed.

Caterpillar Collector Profile: Ed Claessen

Both Ed Claessen and his wife Sue grew up in Waverly, Minnesota, and have lived in the area ever since. Waverly is a friendly town about thirty miles west of Minneapolis. The Claessen "ranch" is out in the country, which allows running room for son Dan and Claessen's Caterpillar collection.

Claessen has been in the construction business for twenty-five years since he bought and rescued a 1930 Cat Sixty. As a boy, Claessen would hitch rides on county graders and other machinery driven by his dad's best friend. The friend showed Claessen how to operate the machines. Now he has a track loader, wheel loader, D6C, and a non-Caterpillar excavator.

Claessen is also an expert on the details of the Best and Caterpillar Sixty tractors and has published articles on the subject. He is a collector of books and literature on the subject of Caterpillar.

machine with great success—in fact, it attracted so much attention in Hungary he decided to import Holt tractors. In 1912, he was awarded the dealership for the Austro-Hungarian Empire and Germany.

Armed with his new Holts, Steiner aggressively challenged all comers to plowing and pulling contests throughout his territory. The success of the Caterpillar tractors over regular wheeled tractors soon caught the attention of the Austrian and German military. Further demonstrations were ordered, but the German military was not convinced. Their opinion changed in 1913, and Steiner was ordered by the Austrian and German military to import all the Caterpillar tractors he could get—and to look into licensing manufacturing rights.

On June 28, 1914, the Crown Prince of Austria was assassinated in the city of Sarajevo, Serbia, and Austria-Hungary declared war on Serbia. Because of a network of mutual defense treaties, other countries were dragged into the conflict on both sides, sparking World War I.

Fortunately for the Allies, the Germans had delayed their decision to order Holt machines via Steiner long enough for the war to break out; all trade with the Central Powers came to a halt before more than a few Caterpillar tractors were delivered. The British Army had meanwhile heard word of the Caterpillar tractor's prowess and immediately asked Holt engineers to bring tractors to England for demonstrations.

The U.S. War Department did not consent to test the Holt until 1915—and then only after Great Britain, France, and Russia had pointed the way by ordering more than one thousand Caterpillars for their war efforts. The War Department still held to the old-fashioned philosophy that only animal power was reliable for war use. In 1916, the U.S. Army changed its way of thinking and purchased twenty-seven Caterpillar tractors.

The U.S. Army Caterpillar tractors were soon pressed into service when President Woodrow Wilson ordered General John "Black Jack" Pershing to invade Mexico in a punitive foray against Mexican revolutionary outlaw hero Francisco "Pancho" Villa. In retaliation for the United States's support of the presidency of Villa's enemy Venustiano Carranza, Villa had raided the New Mexico town of Columbus, killing American citizens and destroying part of the village. While Pershing's expedition failed to capture Villa, the Caterpillar tractors won honors. They were instrumental in

1913 C. L. Best 75
Although it was an unabashed copy of the Holt 75, C. L. Best's 75 had significant improvements, mainly in its metallurgy. C. L. Best made its own engines from 1912 on.

conveying troops and supplies some 350 miles (560 km) into then-roadless Mexico. Resounding praise from Pershing for the Caterpillars gave them credibility with the army.

Meanwhile, Holts were proving their mettle—and metal—on two fronts in the European war as well. The big crawlers had been virtually unstoppable, even in adverse conditions on the fields of Flanders. Allied Caterpillars were also being suited in armor plating to enable them to pull artillery into firing positions.

The Caterpillar's battleworthiness inspired British Army Colonel Earnest D. Swinton to order the British Foster company to build a completely armored tracked vehicle, soon known as a "tank." The crawler track system used on the Foster tank was licensed from Holt but, in an ironic twist, its design was drafted by English engineer David Roberts. In 1896, Roberts had been an employee of the British Hornsby-Akroid firm that had tried unsuccessfully to sell the British War Office a wheeled military tractor. In 1904, Roberts adapted his patented track sys-

tem to the military tractor, but again there was little interest from the British Army. The patents were then sold to Holt, which now licensed them back to the British.

The British Foster tanks were first used in September 1916 in the Battle of the Somme in France. They rolled over impenetrable German trenches dug deep into the earth of the battlefield, changing warfare forever. Following the War To End All Wars, American newspapers gave undue credit to Holt for the development of the tank; Colonel Swinton also lavished praise on Holt, calling the firm's Stockton works "the cradle of the tank."

Setting the Stage for the Postwar Years

The war years were tough on the C. L. Best Tractor Company, as Best found it impossible to win U.S. government contracts for its tractors. What Best did not know was that the cousin of Holt Vice President and General Manager Murray Baker was the principle they had to sell to at the War Department.

After its efforts proved fruitless, Best concentrated in-

C. L. Best 75, circa 1915
A 75 pulls a 12-ton (10,800-kg) load of supplies in the Canadian Northwest Territories. (Glenbow Archives)

stead on selling to farmers, leaving military work entirely to Holt. Holt's production was completely focused on the government, while Best's was completely commercial. After the United States entered the war on April 6, 1917, however, Best was unable to obtain steel for commercial ventures. Nevertheless, Best's field men worked hard with construction crews, farmers, and logging operators, gaining valuable operating experience and cementing relationships.

Many of Best's customers were also investors in the company. When the wartime steel shortage hit, investments were not paying off, and these customer-investors began to get nervous. This state of affairs would soon prove dire to C. L. Best.

Best showed one of two prototypes of its new Model 8/16 at a San Francisco exposition in 1915, and because of the hard times, the firm sold one of the tractors after the show to a Cleveland businessman named Rollin White. Along with two of his brothers, White had his fingers in numerous projects: He was manufacturing the White

Steamer automobile, running the White Sewing Machine Company, developing a gas engine, and starting the Cleveland Motor Plow Company with the goal of building a farm tractor. The Whites were so impressed by the little Best 8/16 that they bought Best's company. Offering a quick return on investments, the Whites succeeded in convincing Best's disgruntled investors to sell out until the White brothers held controlling interest in the C. L. Best Tractor Company. Only after bitter proxy and stock battles was C. L. Best able to regain control of his namesake firm.

The 8/16 was gone for good, however. Rollin White copied Best's prototype and created an even lighter-weight tractor, which he named the Cletrac, short for the Cleveland Tractor Company. Best also lost several of his firm's patents and engineers to White during the ownership battle. Thus, from 1916 on, Best tractors used the master clutch and steering clutch-brake control method rather than the differential-brake steering of the 8/16, which was now a prime feature of the Cletracs.

Above: 1920s C. L. Best 25
The 25 accompanied the 60 and 75 in the C. L. Best line.

Below: 1913 C. L. Best "Humpback" 30
Designed for orchard use, the 30 was called the "Humpback" because of the staggered upper drive sprocket. Some seven decades later, this configuration again made its appearance on modern High Drive Caterpillars.

1920s C. L. Best Sixty brochure
Logging remained a prime market for Holt and C. L. Best for many decades.

1920 C. L. Best Sixty
This Sixty has the original-style horizontal control levers. Note the exposed spinning flywheel.

1920 C. L. Best Sixty
From the rear, the dual-back "Logger" seat is visible. The smaller tank on top of the gas tank is for oil to lube the sprockets.

Armored Holt military crawlers, circa 1918
Fitted with armor-plated bodywork, Holt crawlers served the U.S. Army as artillery gun carriages. (Photograph © J. C. Allen & Son)

Despite the ownership dispute with White and Holt's valuable military contracts, Best was in a much better position than Holt when World War I ended in 1918. Holt had spent its efforts in redesigning its products to meet government requirements, which were not necessarily suited for commercial use. Now, government activities and contracts were terminated. Holt came out of the war with its tillerless 10-Ton and 5-Ton models and smaller T-35. But to make matters worse for Holt, it found itself inundated with partially finished government tractors and cancelled orders for which Holt would not be paid. Further, the U.S. Army packed up all the Holt tractors it had in France, returned them to the United States at great taxpayer expense, and sold them as surplus at rock-bottom prices.

Meanwhile Best had good machines already in production when World War I ended, including the Model 75, 30-hp Muley, and a new Model 40. While Best had been hurt financially during the war, the firm found a ready market in 1918.

Best also had good new models in development. In 1919, the new Best 60 was offered for sale. Known interchangeably as the 60 or Sixty, the machine was a truly modern crawler engineered with all of the lessons learned during the previous decade. This classic Tracklayer would set the stage for the next several decades of tracked tractor development.

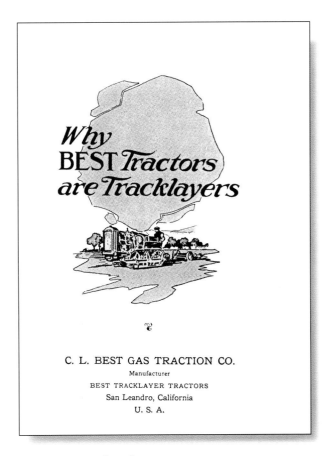

1920s C. L. Best brochure

Above: 1925 C. L. Best Thirty Orchard
Upon introduction, the Thirty was originally called the Model S. It was built by C. L. Best and Caterpillar between 1921 and 1932, when more than 23,000 were sold. Owner: Jerry Gast.

Right: 1925 C. L. Best Thirty Orchard
C. L. Best tractors used the trade name "Tracklayer" to distinguish them from the Holt Caterpillars.

Facing page: 1920 C. L. Best Sixty
Best made its own durable four-cylinder engine for the famous Sixty. Bore and stroke were 6.50x8.50 inches (162.50x212.50 mm). Rated operating speed was a mere 650 rpm.

КАТЕРПИЛЛАР

1920s Russian Caterpillar logo

Above: Holt Caterpillar Thirty, 1931
Between October 1929 and May 1930, Holt sold more than $12 million worth of machines to the Soviet Union, providing Caterpillar with much-needed cash flow during the Great Depression.

Right: Holt Caterpillars in Russia, circa 1919
Following Benjamin Holt's sales tour of Russia, numerous Holt crawlers made their way to the new communist country.

Above: 1920s C. L. Best 60
An image of the 60 from a C. L. Best brochure.

Above: Holt Caterpillar 45 and Deere plows, 1916
Holt crawlers were used to pull two three-bottom John Deere plows in this plowing demonstration. (Deere & Company)

Left: 1923 C. L. Best advertisement
According to this dramatic ad promoting the Thirty and Sixty, "Best Tractors 'Can be relied upon'" to plow up to a 70-percent grade.

Above: 1925 C. L. Best Thirty Orchard
The Thirty was powered by a 461-ci (7,551-cc), four-cylinder engine that made 38 belt hp. Rated engine speed was 850 rpm.

Left: 1925 C. L. Best Thirty Orchard
When introduced in 1921, the Thirty was one of the most modern crawlers. It was agile and reliable, and found use in logging, farming, and orchards.

Above: 1925 C. L. Best Thirty Orchard
Clayton Gast, son of owner Jerry Gast, points out the low seat of the Thirty Orchard.

Right: 1925 C. L. Best Thirty Orchard
The Best Thirty used a four-cylinder overhead-valve engine with a bore and stroke of 4.75x6.50 inches (118.75x162.50 mm). It was originally built with a two-speed transmission; later versions had three-speed transmissions.

Holt 45, 1920s
Designed especially for Midwestern farmers, the Peoria-built 45 was made with both wide front wheels or a single front wheel. This one was used on a farm to power a corn chopper. (Smithsonian Institution)

Above: 1929 Ziegler Caterpillar logo

The Ziegler logo graces a 1929 Caterpillar Fifteen. The dealer has developed a reputation for being responsive to the needs of Cat equipment owners whether they have a single piece of antique machinery or millions of dollars worth of the latest earthmovers.

Left: Ziegler Caterpillar display, 1960s

The William H. Ziegler Company, Inc., is one of the world's largest Caterpillar dealers. Headquartered in Bloomington, Minnesota, its territory stretches throughout the state and into Iowa. Ziegler started selling the C. L. Best machines in the 1920s, and now covers Cat's full line of products from maritime and mining powerplants to agricultural, logging, and construction equipment. This display of Cat power was on show at the Minnesota State Fair in the 1950s.

CHAPTER 4

The Birth of Caterpillar

The Founding of the Caterpillar Tractor Company, 1920–1933

Above: 1930s Caterpillar toy
This miniature crawler measures 8 inches (20 cm) in length. Owner: Robert Stewart.

Left: 1926 Caterpillar Sixty
In its heyday, the Sixty was considered the industry standard for large crawlers by farmers and loggers. Owner: Dave Smith.

Times were tough in the tractor industry following World War I. Both Holt and Best were dogged by huge burdens of debt after the war. Operating capital was obtained by long lines of credit from financial institutions, and it was common practice to refinance these loans periodically, sometimes by borrowing from other institutions. At the same time, the two companies had considerable excess manufacturing capacity, especially Holt's operation in Peoria. Then, in December 1920, Benjamin Holt died suddenly. Meanwhile a general postwar recession had set in, hitting farmers particularly hard. A dramatic tractor price war ensued, with the price of Henry Ford's venerable Fordson finally dropping to an astonishing $395 in 1922. The price war did not affect the sales of the larger crawlers, but where wheeled tractors would do the job, the price difference all but eliminated the chance of selling a crawler.

Holt and Best both had solid connections with large banking houses. Holt mainly financed through the Boston firm of Bond and Goodwin, while Best used the San Francisco firm of Pierce, Fair and Company. These firms had representatives on the tractor companies' boards of directors. With the death of Benjamin Holt, a banker from Bond and Goodman, Thomas Baxter, was elected by the Holt board to Benjamin Holt's vacant position of president. Murray Baker of the Peoria factory was the heir apparent, but Baxter held the handle on the money machine.

Harry Fair of Pierce, Fair and Company had a seat on the Best board. Fair had also invested personal funds in Best. He was rightly concerned about his own as well as his banking house's money because of the downturn in the tractor market and excess manufacturing capacity. Fair made secret overtures to Pliny Holt and Murray Baker about combining the two crawler makers. He pointed out that there was ample business for one firm but not two, and Pierce, Fair and Company could provide all the funding that would be needed.

The Holt board called a meeting and laid out the plan. Naturally, Thomas Baxter resigned, and longtime corporate attorney Charles Neumiller was elected in his place. All stock was then passed to a group including Pierce, Fair and Company and "associates" such as the Holt family, Murray Baker, and the Holt company. This group then transferred their assets to a new corporation, the Caterpillar Tractor Company. The owners of the C. L. Best Gas Tractor Company did the same at a meeting in San Leandro.

Thus, the Caterpillar Tractor Company was born in 1925. Neither Best nor Holt had sold out, and it was not really a merger in the proper sense. It was in truth a consolidation, in which the two firms reorganized their financial ownership. That this consolidation was the right decision was reflected in improved sales and profits from 1925 until the effects of the Great Depression were felt. Best executives obtained the most influential positions in the new company, probably due to the influence of Harry Fair.

The new company now boasted an excellent line of tractors, made up of the premier machines from Best and Holt. Best's Sixty and Thirty were carried over, as were Holt's small 2-Ton, 5-Ton, and 10-Ton machines. Tractor manufacturing was consolidated at Peoria and San Leandro. A subsidiary, the Western Harvester Company, built combines at the Stockton plant.

1930s Caterpillar brochure
The new Caterpillar company switched to Highway Yellow paint for its machines in December 1931. This ad shows the second gasoline-powered Holt built, number 1002, undergoing factory tests in 1908.

The Caterpillar-Deere Crawler Lineage

Brothers Jesse and Harry Lindeman entered the farm implement business in 1923 by buying out the bankrupt Yakima, Washington, dealer that Jesse worked for. Things went well for the brothers, who serviced apple and cherry growers in the area, and so in 1924 they decided to take on a Holt Caterpillar dealership.

The Lindemans were just hitting their stride by late 1925 when Holt and Best merged. At that time, Holt and Best each had about a hundred dealerships. Many of the dealers were in the same towns and had been competing with each other for several decades. Now difficult choices had to be made, choices that meant stripping dealerships from about half of the dealers, loyal friends, and business associates. Territories had to be large enough to allow the surviving dealerships both to prosper and to offer the level of support expected of them. Caterpillar insisted on the dealerships' ability to provide parts and service for machines in the field. Dealers were required to fill 85 percent of parts orders from their stock, a requirement that still exists today. Mergers of competing dealerships were encouraged, but were often difficult to work out.

In the Yakima area, there was a Best dealership that the Lindemans had been fiercely battling with for orchard business. As a result of the merger, the new Caterpillar firm had to streamline its Best and Holt dealers, and since the Yakima-area Best dealership was the oldest, the Lindeman brothers were out. By the end of 1925, Caterpillar had narrowed its list to eighty-nine domestic and foreign dealers.

The Lindemans had learned a lot during their time selling and servicing Holts. And they had loyal customers who still needed crawlers. So, being handy with a wrench, they acquired a wheeled John Deere Model D tractor and grafted tracks from a Best Thirty onto it.

This conversion caught the eye of Deere & Company of Moline, Illionois, and the Lindeman brothers were contracted to convert a short run of Deere Model Ds into orchard DO crawlers. The Lindemans next created Deere Model GPO-L orchard crawlers, followed by the famous Model BO-L crawler.

On January 1, 1947, Deere bought Lindeman Power Equipment and the Yakima works continued to add tracks to Deere's wheeled tractors. In the process, the Lindemans became the fathers of the Deere crawler line, providing stiff competition for Caterpillar even today.

Holt's Contributions to Caterpillar:
Holt T-35/2-Ton

Holt's T-35 was developed before the consolidation under the leadership of Harmon Eberhard. Thomas Baxter replaced Benjamin Holt as president and turned the company toward building smaller tractors, which he saw as the future for farming, logging, and construction. The T-35 designation was soon changed to 2-Ton to be in line with Holt nomenclature.

The 2-Ton featured a unique overhead-camshaft, four-cylinder gas engine. The 4.00x5.00-inch (100x125-mm) engine displaced 251 ci (4,111 cc). Rated engine speed was 1,000 rpm. The transmission offered one reverse and three forward speeds. A unique feature of this tractor was that the transmission was located behind the rear axle, rather than in front, as was usual. Oil-cooled steering clutches were used, at least at first. Cast track links were also used. Holt, and later Caterpillar, made all components of the tractor, except for the Eisemann magneto and Kingston carburetor.

In working trim, the tractor weighed 4,000 pounds (1,800 kg), hence the designation "2-Ton." Tractors, like people, tend to gain weight as they get older, and the 2-Ton was more of a 2.5-ton (2,250-kg) machine by the end of its production life. The maximum drawbar pull was 3,275 pounds (1,474 kg).

The 2-Ton was promoted as a compact unit for earthmoving and agriculture. Originally expected to be a 35-hp tractor, it was actually rated at 15 drawbar and 25 belt hp. It was the smallest tractor in the product line through most of the 1920s. The 2-Ton was built first by Holt and then by Caterpillar, staying in production from 1921 to 1928. List price in 1927 was $1,850.

LA CHENILLE

1920s French Caterpillar logo

HOUSENKA

1920s Czechoslovakian Caterpillar logo

ГУСЕНИЦА

1920s Russian Caterpillar logo

RAUPE

1920s German Caterpillar logo

Facing page, top: 1927 Caterpillar 2-Ton
Holt's T-35 made its debut in 1921, but the designation was soon changed to 2-Ton to line it up with the other Holt tractors, the 5-Ton and 10-Ton. The model was carried through the merger and became the Caterpillar 2-Ton after 1925. Owner: Terry Anderson.

Facing page, bottom: 1927 Caterpillar 2-Ton
The 251-ci (4,111-cc), four-cylinder, overhead-cam engine of the 2-Ton measured 4.00x5.00 inches (100x125 mm). It produced 25 belt hp.

1920s Holt Caterpillar T-35 advertisement
The T-35 was "The Supreme Small Tractor," according to this ad, and could be viewed by potential buyers at state or county fairs everywhere. The T-35's price was a mere $375.

Above: 1927 Caterpillar 2-Ton
Owner Terry Anderson spent four years restoring this 2-Ton.

Right: 1927 Caterpillar 2-Ton
When introduced by Holt, the T-35 was planned as a 35-hp tractor, but it was actually rated at 15 drawbar and 25 belt hp.

Facing page: 1927 Caterpillar 2-Ton
Holt, and later Caterpillar, made all of the components of the 2-Ton, except for the carburetor and magneto.

Above: 1927 Caterpillar 2-Ton
This restored 2-Ton retains its original rubber-block track pads.

Left: 1927 Caterpillar 2-Ton
The 2-Ton boasted a substantial air cleaner. This unit was missing when owner Terry Anderson acquired the tractor, and locating a replacement was quite a challenge.

Below: 1930s Caterpillar dealer clock
Owner: Larry Maasdam.

Caterpillar 2-Ton and Combined Harvester, 1928
A new Caterpillar 2-Ton powers an older Holt Combined Harvester through a Midwestern soybean field. (Photograph © J. C. Allen & Son)

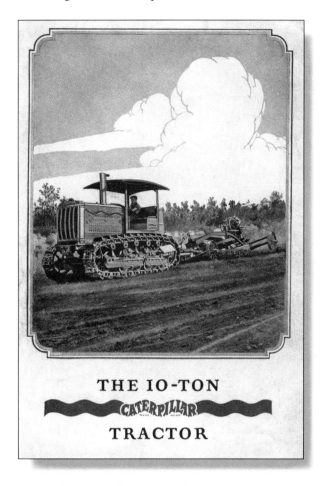

1920s Holt Caterpillar 10-Ton brochure

Holt 5-Ton

The Model 5-Ton was an outgrowth of the old 25/45 model that was developed during World War I under the guiding hand of the U.S. Army. It was first sold to the public in 1919. Although named the 5-Ton, the crawler actually weighed a little less than 10,000 pounds (4,500 kg) in working trim.

The 5-Ton boasted a three-speed transmission with a top traveling speed of about 7 mph (11.2 kph), which was incredibly fast for a crawler of those times. A Holt-designed overhead-valve, four-cylinder engine of 425 ci (6,962 cc) provided power.

Holt 10-Ton

The Model 10-Ton weighed in at 9.5 tons (8,550 kg). The tractor was developed under the auspices of the U.S. Army during World War I. As on the 5-Ton, it had a peculiar two-segment bogey-wheel carrier, favored by the Army because of its higher speed capabilities and better trench-crossing ability. This feature could cause tracks to slip off when reversing with a heavy load, however.

An overhead-valve, four-cylinder engine of 929 ci (15,217 cc) was used. A three-speed transmission gave speeds of just under 2 mph in first, about 3 mph in second, and 6 mph in third (3.2, 4.8, and 9.6 kph). Maximum engine power was 55 hp.

1922 Holt Caterpillar 5-Ton
The earlier version, the 1920 Holt 5-Ton Model T-11, rode on a two-segment track rail system, was rated at 40 belt hp, and weighed just under 10,000 pounds (4,500 kg). This later Model T-29 version of the 5-Ton used a one-piece track frame.

Above: 1920s Holt Caterpillar 10-Ton
The 10-Ton was developed with the help of the U.S. Army during World War I. Owners: Volk family of St. Stephen, Minnesota.

Left: 1920s Holt Caterpillar 10-Ton
The 10-Ton was powered by an overhead-valve, four-cylinder engine of 929 ci (15,217 cc). Maximum power was 55 hp.

1910s Holt 10-Ton
A Holt 10-Ton encased in heavy armor plating as used by the U.S. Army during World War I. This restored military crawler was on display at the 1999 LeSeuer County Pioneer Power Show. (Photograph © Robert N. Pripps)

Best Contributions to Caterpillar:
Best Model A/Sixty

Initially known as the Model A, the Sixty was a well-balanced tractor that was extremely agile for its size. It was considerably lighter and had less power than the Best Model 75 it replaced, but the Sixty could work circles around the 75.

Power came from a 6.50x8.50-inch (162.50x212.50-mm), four-cylinder, overhead-valve engine. Gas was the standard fuel, but kerosene equipment was optional. Rated engine speed was 650 rpm. A two-speed transmission with one reverse gear was standard; a three-speed unit was optional. When first tested at the University of Nebraska in 1921 as Test No. 76, the Sixty was not able to achieve its namesake rating of 60 belt hp, and was accordingly rated at 35 drawbar and 55 belt hp. Test weight was 17,500 pounds (7,875 kg).

The Sixty was tested again in 1923 as No. 98, and by then improvements in the engine allowed a full 40/60 rating. The Sixty as tested this time sported a three-speed

transmission, and test weight was up to 18,580 pounds (8,361 kg). Another test was run in 1924 as No. 105, and maximum brake power was up to 73 hp, due to more improvements in the cam timing. Weight was up to 20,000 pounds (9,000 kg), and the three-speed transmission was now standard.

Early versions of the Model A had the low, orchard-type seat with steering clutch levers out to the right side over the fender. This arrangement worked fine for agriculture and construction, but for logging, the springy, far-aft, low-mounted seat gave a thrilling ride over rough, unprepared terrain. Therefore, a high-seat logging version—known as the Model Sixty Cruiser—was added to the line, which also used straight clutch control levers. The high-seat became standard in 1922 at serial number 1126A. A side-by-side, two-seat Cruiser was also offered.

The Sixty was produced by Best and Caterpillar from 1919 through 1931. Selling price was reduced from around $6,000 to a low of $4,000 by the end of production.

1926 Caterpillar Sixty
Introduced in 1919 by C. L. Best, the Sixty became the Caterpillar Sixty after the 1925 merger. It overwhelmed the competition because of its reliable, well-balanced design.

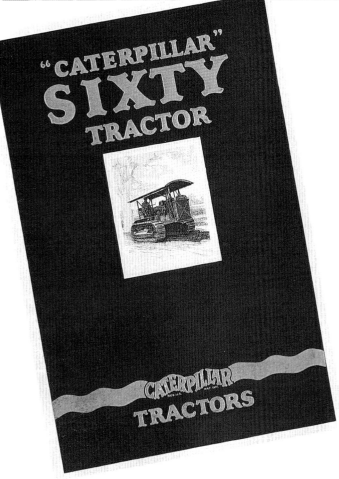

Above: 1926 Caterpillar Sixty

The wavy "Caterpillar" logo was first seen on Holt crawlers in about 1917. It was not included on new models shortly after the paint was changed from gray to Highway Yellow in 1931. This Sixty, serial number 3331A, was manufactured in San Leandro, California. Owner: Dave Smith.

Left: 1920s Caterpillar Sixty manual

Facing page: 1926 Caterpillar Sixty

Brass components were common on the Sixty engine.

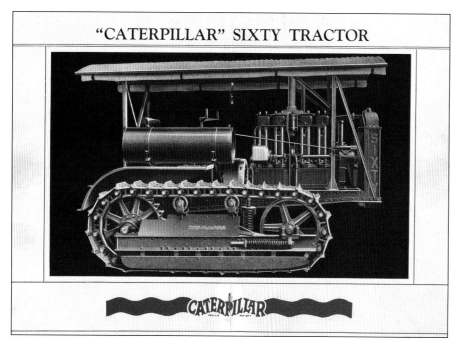

1920s Caterpillar Sixty brochure
The cylinder above the fender was the massive fuel tank, which a hard-working Sixty could easily empty in a ten-hour day.

1926 Caterpillar Sixty
This Sixty spent about 2,000 hours working on a California wheat farm, pulling plows and a Holt No. 36 Combined Harvester. It was still wearing its original tracks when acquired by Dave Smith, one of the founders of the Antique Caterpillar Machinery Owner's Club.

1926 Caterpillar Sixty
The legendary Sixty is one of the best known and most widely respected of all antique tractors. This venerable Sixty is in original, unrestored condition, showing the wear and tear of a life of hard work. Owner: Kevin Kalsem.

1931 Caterpillar Magazine
A Caterpillar Sixty with a LaPlant-Choate V-plow, snow wings, and cab earns its living.

Above: 1926 Caterpillar Sixty
From the first versions built by C. L. Best in 1919 through the end of production under the Caterpillar name in 1931, almost 14,000 were built.

Right: 1930s Caterpillar Sixty manual

"Logging"
Lassen County, California

Above: Logging in Lassen County, California

A Caterpillar Sixty brings in a giant redwood log, circa 1930. Note the operator is wearing dust goggles. (Eastman Collection, University of California–Davis)

Left: 1915 Holt 45

The 45 weighed 14,000 pounds (6,300 kg). It was powered by a 6.00x7.00-inch (150x175-mm), four-cylinder engine producing 45 hp at 600 rpm. The two-speed transmission provided speeds of 2.18 and 2.93 mph (3.49 and 4.69 kph).

1915 Holt 45

The 45 sold new for $2,750. Owner Larry Maasdam bought this 45 from Harlan Thompson of Harper, Kansas, who had farmed with the Holt for twenty-five years.

1930 Caterpillar Thirty
The radiator of the Thirty was an impressive piece of architecture that spoke of the hard labor these machines could perform.

Best Model S/Thirty

Originally known as the Best Model S, this crawler later came to be called the Thirty. It replaced the Model B, also known as the Twenty-Five.

A four-cylinder, overhead-valve gas engine provided power at a rated speed of 800 rpm. With a bore and stroke of 4.75x6.50 inches (118.75x162.50 mm), the engine displaced 461 ci (7,551 cc). Originally built with a two-speed transmission, later versions had three speeds.

The Thirty was tested at the University of Nebraska in 1921 as Test No. 77 and was rated at 18 drawbar and 30 belt hp. In order to make its namesake belt rating of 30 hp, it was necessary to enlarge the carburetor, advance the timing, and run the engine at 810 rpm. Test weight was 7,400 pounds (3,330 kg).

Tested again in 1923 as No. 99, it achieved a 20/30 rating without resorting to modifications. The Thirty was tested again in 1924 as No. 104, and the rated engine speed was now 850 rpm. This speed increase, plus cam timing and carburetor changes, allowed the tractor to comfortably exceed 30 belt hp—in fact, 37.83 hp was recorded. Test weight was 9,065 pounds (4,079 kg).

1930 Caterpillar Thirty
Introduced by C. L. Best in 1921, the Thirty was built by Caterpillar until 1932 and manufactured in large numbers due to their popularity. This one is serial number PS13887. Owner: Jerry Gast.

1930 Caterpillar Thirty

Following serial number PS13286, later Thirtys such as this one have engines with the cylinders in pairs, rather than four individual cylinders. They also boast two separate cylinder heads and are known as "Two-Head" Thirtys.

Early tractors were low-seat, also known as tail-seat, models built especially for orchards and other agriculture uses. Steering levers extended out over the right fender to accommodate left-hand control as the operator looked back over his or her right shoulder at the implement. The Thirty was originally built without a canopy, but full canopies were soon offered for agricultural models. Logging versions usually did not have canopies, but had high-mounted bench seats and straight steering levers.

The Thirty was an agile tractor with modern features. It proved to be reliable and dependable for logging, construction, and agriculture. It was available with a variety of options, including a front-shaft power takeoff (PTO). When equipped with the front PTO, a hand crank extending from the rear of the tractor was provided.

The Model S and Thirty was built from 1921 through 1932. A total of 23,827 were built by Best and Caterpillar; of these, 9,535 were built in San Leandro.

1930 Caterpillar Thirty

Wide-gauge Thirtys such as this one were designed to work on steep hillsides. This Thirty wears angle shoes, also known as "swamp pads." It was purchased from ninety-year-old logger Harry Smith of Holiday, Missouri. Owner Jerry Gast reported that the tractor had been repeatedly repaired by welding: valve stems and seats were all welded, as was the carburetor needle valve. Gast also said that he took 10 gallons (38 liters) of mud out of the final drives upon restoration, attesting to the hard life this Thirty had lived.

Above: 1932 Caterpillar Thirty
A late "Two-Head" Thirty. Starting in 1931, Caterpillars were painted in the now-classic Highway Yellow. Owner: Alan Smith.

Left: 1932 Caterpillar Thirty
This Thirty rides on "bog shoes," which were special treads Smith had made to original Caterpillar drawings.

1932 Caterpillar dealer sign
Owner: Larry Maasdam.

The Best of Both Worlds: Caterpillar Twenty

The neat little Caterpillar Twenty was the first all-new Caterpillar tractor after the company was formed in 1925. The Twenty had its roots in the Best engineering department, however, and replaced the venerable 2-Ton in the product lineup.

The overhead-valve, four-cylinder engine featured a 4.00x5.50-inch (100x137.50-mm) bore and stroke, displacing 277 ci (4,537 cc). The gearbox had three forward speeds. By giving the Twenty excess capability, Caterpillar avoided the Nebraska test ratings trap that it had fallen into when the Sixty could not make its 60-hp rating. The new machine easily achieved 29 hp on the belt test. Half fenders with a long, curved downturn at the rear characterized the tractor.

The Twenty was built both in San Leandro and in Peoria. San Leandro tractors had black lettering and used a "P" serial number prefix; Peoria lettering was red and the prefix "PL" was used. The Twenty was marketed from 1927 to 1931.

1931 Caterpillar Twenty
The Twenty was the first new design built after the merger of Holt and C. L. Best in 1925. It was introduced in 1927 and remained in production until 1931. Owner: Larry Maasdam.

Caterpillar Collector Profile: Kevin Kalsem

Another of the younger Cat collectors, Kevin Kalsem is just thirty-four years old and makes his living as a trucker. His collection includes a Caterpillar Sixty, two Cat Tens, a Fifteen, a Twenty, and two Caterpillar combines. He is also a collector of Caterpillar literature.

Kalsem is an expert on crawler history in general and especially the Caterpillar Sixty. His father has a large salvage yard that specializes in combines of all description.

1927 Caterpillar Twenty announcement

1932 Caterpillar Thirty
The Thirty was powered by a four-cylinder, overhead-valve gas engine measuring 4.75x6.50 inches (118.75x162.50 mm) to displace 461 ci (7,551 cc).

1920s Caterpillar magazine

1931 Caterpillar Twenty
The four-cylinder, overhead-valve engine of the Twenty had a bore and stroke of 4.00x5.50 inches (100x137.50 mm) that operated at 1,100 rpm.

Caterpillar Ten

Introduced in 1928, the Ten (PT) was the smallest Caterpillar tractor. Its side-valve, four-cylinder engine had a bore and stroke of 3.375x4.00 inches (84.375x100 mm), displacing 143 ci (2,342 cc). Unlike the 2-Ton, dry clutches were employed. A high-clearance agricultural version was made that had an extra gear set in the final drives; the bevel gear set was turned over so that the right rotation at the tracks was maintained. Gauge widths of 37 and 44 inches (92.50 and 110 cm) were offered.

In Nebraska Tractor Test No. 160, the Ten was rated at 10 drawbar and 15 belt hp. Maximum brake horsepower was 18. The Ten was made in Peoria from 1928 to 1932.

Right: 1928 Caterpillar Ten advertisement

Below: 1933 Caterpillar Ten
Owner Marv Fery shows Gail Koenig how to drive his restored Ten, the smallest of the Caterpillars. This Ten is serial number PT3609.

ANNOUNCING THE "CATERPILLAR" TEN

A smaller size of the "Caterpillar" Tractor than has ever before been offered ...eagerly awaited by all small-power users...first pre-viewed on September 1st, 1928...ready for deliveries early in 1929 ... price will be announced later.

1930s Caterpillar Ten
Caterpillar built almost 5,000 Tens from 1928 to 1932. This one has a dandy sun umbrella. Owner: Kevin Kalsem.

1931 Caterpillar Ten
This Ten was fitted with a highway mower kit and painted Highway Yellow. (Smithsonian Institution)

1930s Caterpillar Ten
The Ten was one of the few Caterpillars to use a side-valve engine. Note the big six-volt headlights. Owner: Kevin Kalsem.

1930 Caterpillar Ten
The Ten's side-valve, four-cylinder engine had a bore and stroke of 3.375x4.00 inches (84.375x100 mm), displacing 143 ci (2,342 cc).

1930 Caterpillar Ten
The Ten was rated at 10 drawbar and 15 belt hp. Owners: Richard and Carol Schmidt.

1928 Caterpillar Ten advertisement

1930s Caterpillar Fifteen
The Caterpillar Fifteen (PV Series) was a scaled-up Model Ten. These are referred to as "Big" Fifteens to differentiate them from the Fifteen 7C Series, or the "Small" Fifteen, which was the same size as the Ten. This Big Fifteen is serial number PV6769. Owner: Robert Stewart.

Caterpillar Fifteen

The Cat Fifteen (PV) was essentially a scaled-up companion to the Ten. It featured a 3.75x5.00-inch (93.75x125-mm) engine displacing 220 ci (3,604 cc) and turning a respectable 1,500 rpm. The transmission offered one reverse and three forward speeds. Weight was 5,500 pounds (2,475 kg).

Larger dry clutches than those used on the Ten forced the Fifteen to be about 12 inches (30 cm) wider. Gauge widths of 40 and 50 inches (100 and 125 cm) were available. Kerosene fuel was optional, requiring the addition of a starting gas tank and plumbing. A high-clearance option was available as a kit.

In 1932, a 7C version of the Fifteen was introduced as a direct replacement for the Ten. This model featured the 3.375x4.00-inch (84.375x100-mm) engine and weighed 4,500 pounds (2,025 kg).

The Fifteen was made between 1928 and 1933. In 1932, it cost $1,100.

1929 Caterpillar advertisement

1930s Caterpillar Fifteen
The Caterpillar Model Fifteen PV Series was built between 1929 and 1932. The last of these left the factory in Highway Yellow paint.

1920s Caterpillar Ten and Fifteen brochure

CHAPTER 5

New Technology for New Times

Caterpillar
» FARM TRACTORS «

The Development of Diesel Power, 1925–1945

Above: **1934 Caterpillar dealer sign**
Owner: Larry Maasdam.

Left: **1930s Caterpillar Model Twenty-Two Orchard**
The streamlined fenders of the Model Twenty-Two Orchard were designed to let the tractor slip through low-hanging branches without getting caught. Owner: Larry Maasdam.

The stock market crash of 1929 that ushered in the Great Depression was exacerbated by a severe drought in the Great Plains. Along with the halting of many construction projects due to the economic downturn, farm income dropped worldwide, and tractor sales subsequently plummeted. By 1932, Caterpillar booked a loss for the year of $1.6 million. U.S. tractor sales in 1932 dropped to 19,000 units, the fewest since 1915. Of the forty-eight tractor makers in 1929, less than ten survived through 1933.

Caterpillar was among the survivors. Its survival was due in large part to sales to Bolshevik Russia. Holt Caterpillar tractors had a good reputation for reliability in Russia as far back as 1913. In 1919, soon after the revolution, the ruling Communists initiated a drive to mechanize food production and organized huge collective farms, some with a half million acres (200,000 hectares). The Russian government's Zernotrest ("Grain Trust"), through its buying agent, Amtorg ("American Trading Company"), ordered mostly wheeled tractors, but for the largest farms, twenty Caterpillar Sixtys were purchased. These were so successful that 1,350 more were ordered, as well as Thirtys, Twentys, and combines. Nevertheless, 1932 was the first unprofitable year for Caterpillar—but it had survived.

New Decade, New Products

Despite the grim times in the early 1930s, Caterpillar management knew that new product was required to remain competitive. Allis-Chalmers, with its Monarch line, and Cletrac were pressing hard, and each had models in direct competition with Caterpillar. In 1929, Foote Bros. Gear & Machine Company of Chicago had taken over the successful line of Steel Mule crawlers made by the Bates Machine & Tractor Company of Joliet, Illinois. Rumors began in 1930 that the giant International Harvester Company of Chicago was considering crawler versions of its popular wheeled tractors. To counter these threats, smart new smaller Caterpillar tractors aimed especially at the farmer were needed.

The first of Caterpillar's new machines was the "small" Fifteen (7C). This was a restyled version of the original Ten (PT1), but engine improvements brought it up to 18 drawbar hp. This Fifteen was built in 1932 and 1933.

The Twenty (8C), which became known as the "Flathead Twenty," followed from 1932 to 1934. This was a re-rated version of the "big" Fifteen (PV1) and was not to be confused with the old overhead-valve Twenty (L1 and PL1). Relocation of the fuel tank behind the engine gave the new Fifteen and Twenty a lower hood and a more modern appearance.

The old overhead-valve Twenty (LI and PL1) became the Twenty-Five (3C) in 1931, with production continuing through 1933. Again, engine improvements brought the power up to over 28 drawbar hp. Therefore, it was again re-rated and renamed the Twenty-Eight (4F) in 1933. Production of the Twenty-Eight ended in 1935.

In 1934, the old Flathead Twenty was re-fitted with a new 4.00x5.00-inch (100x125-mm) overhead-valve engine, and it became the Twenty-Two (2F). Production of the popular Twenty-Two continued until 1939, long after other models from the old numbering system were discontinued.

A completely new Thirty (6G) came out in 1935. It was renamed the R4 in 1936, and the R4 (6G) continued in production through 1944.

Specialty government orders arrived for the R2, R3, and R5 tractors. The R2 was essentially the same as the Twenty-Two, and about eighty-three were made between 1934 and 1937. The R3 was similar to the Twenty-Eight, and about sixty R3s were made.

The R5 came out in 1934. The first forty or so were the same as the gas Thirty-Five; the rest of the five hundred produced were based upon the gas Forty. After the Diesel Forty became the RD6, the R5 became its gas counterpart. R5 government tractors had foot clutches and steering brakes that were actuated by the steering clutch levers, but not all R5s were special government machines. Some had conventional controls including a hand master clutch, and a foot brake and hand clutch lever for each track. The last R5 was manufactured in 1940.

By 1939, the R2 was no longer a special U.S. government–order machine but the gas counterpart to the new D2.

The last new gas tractor from Caterpillar was the Sixty-Five (2D), built in 1932 and 1933.

Compression Ignition

German engineer Dr. Rudolf Christian Karl Diesel invented the engine that bears his name. Born in 1858 in Paris of German parents, he studied in England and graduated from the Polytechnic School in Munich, Germany. In 1892, he patented an internal-combustion engine that auto-ignited fuel by the heat of compression. While associated with the Krupp firm in Essen, Germany, in 1893, he built the first "Diesel" engine, which was based on Otto's four-cycle principle. The engine proved his theory, but it exploded and nearly killed him. By 1897, the engine was developed to the point where it was commercially viable and many entrepreneurs purchased manufacturing licenses, including St. Louis beer brewer Adolphus Busch. While on a voyage to England in 1913, Rudolf Diesel was lost overboard in the English Channel.

The main advantage of Diesel's engine was its frugal fuel consumption. Due primarily to the large amounts of fuel they required, tractors of more than 60 hp were rare

Above: **Lunch with Caterpillar Twenty-Two, 1936**
Farm workers sit down to eat their lunches in the company of their trusted Twenty-Two on George Kaper's Hamilton Celery farm in Hamilton, Michigan. (Photograph © J. C. Allen & Son)

Left: **1937 Caterpillar Twenty-Two**
The Twenty-Two was virtually the same as the original R2 built for U.S. government orders. The R2 operated on gasoline, while most Twenty-Twos used distillate fuel. Owner: Larry Maasdam.

Above: 1937 Caterpillar Twenty-Two

The Twenty-Two was produced from 1934 to 1939 in the 2F and 1J Series. It was the most successful of the small Cats, with more than 15,000 built. This one is serial number 1J4072SP.

Right: 1937 Caterpillar Twenty-Two

Weighing just under 7,500 pounds (3,375 kg), the Twenty-Two was capable of a drawbar pull of almost 5,000 pounds (2,250 kg) when running on gasoline— an amazing 66 percent of its weight. Owner: Marvin Fery, one of the founders of the Antique Caterpillar Machinery Owner's Club.

1937 Caterpillar Twenty-Two
The Twenty-Two used a four-cylinder, overhead-valve engine of 251 ci (4,111 cc). With a 4.00x5.00-inch (100x125-mm) bore and stroke, the Twenty-Two and its running mate, the R2 5E, featured 25 drawbar hp. A three-speed transmission was standard along with a foot pedal–operated master clutch.

in the late 1920s. Machines like the Caterpillar Sixty were fitted with gigantic fuel tanks, as they easily burned 10 gallons (38 liters) of fuel per hour of heavy work. Even though fuel was relatively cheap at the time, the big Caterpillar tractors still consumed 75 to 100 gallons (285–380 liters) daily. Just having a week's worth of fuel on hand could be a problem. The diesel engine cut fuel use in half.

There are several reasons for the diesel's frugality. First, diesels boast better thermal efficiency. Second, diesels have more volumetric efficiency as their air intake is not restricted by a carburetor or a throttle, so airflow is vastly improved. Third, diesels burn fuel oil, which has more heat value than gasoline. Fourth, while both gas and kerosene engines are partly cooled by running rich, diesels run lean, saving fuel. Diesels can afford to run a leaner mixture ratio as they always get the same amount of air while

engine speed is controlled by the amount of fuel injected.

Diesel's engine operated on low-volatility fuel oil. The fuel was injected into the combustion chamber at the top of the compression stroke and ignited due to the heat of compression. The compression ratio was between 15:1 and 21:1, dramatically higher than for spark-ignition engines. Compression heats the air to around 1,000 degrees Fahrenheit (538 degrees Celsius) at about 600 pounds per square inch (psi). The flash point of fuel oil is 350°F (177°C).

Diesel engines were originally reserved for stationary duties and ship propulsion, as their great weight and fragility prevented their use in mobile environments. As with steam engines, however, metallurgical advances led the way to mobile diesel applications. Steel with a high strength-to-weight ratio was required for internal parts, and new casting techniques were needed for blocks and cylinder heads.

Diesel fuel standards for flash points and factors affecting ignition ease, heat produced, deposits, and cold starting were developed along with the engine. Fuel quality also needed to be controlled and high-grade fuel filters had to be invented.

The first diesel engines required air to be injected with the fuel to insure atomization, a method that did not accommodate much in speed or load changes. Such diesels were restricted to constant-speed, constant-load applications before the 1930s (except for some experimental diesel trucks made by the German Benz company beginning in 1927). The Robert Bosch Company of Germany developed variable-delivery hydraulic fuel injectors that aided mobile use by controlling the engine's speed and power. Perfecting the diesel injector pumps that handled up to 30,000 psi was difficult, as they taxed the technology of the 1930s.

Pliny Holt was among the first to see the benefits of diesel. Although work on diesels had also been done by C. L. Best's engineers before the 1925 merger, neither Best nor Holt had the resources to develop diesel at that time. Immediately after the merger, Pliny Holt set up experiments in both diesel engine manufacture and injector systems, spending more than a million dollars over the next few years. By 1930, Caterpillar's new Research Division had taken over all experiments.

By the end of 1930, a tractor was ready for testing with the new Cat diesel Model D9900 engine—which bore a resemblance to the German Benz company's diesel truck engine. By October 1931, the first Caterpillar diesel was delivered to a customer, giving Caterpillar the distinction of being the first tractor maker in the world to offer a diesel engine. It is possible that this tractor was also the first Highway Yellow Caterpillar tractor, as it was at this time that the gray paint scheme was dropped in favor of the brighter—and more optimistic—color.

By 1933, most of the introductory diesel growing pains were history. Caterpillar built more diesels in 1933 than all other North American manufacturers combined.

Above, top: 1937 Caterpillar Twenty-Two
The last few Twenty-Twos had "Caterpillar" cast into the radiator, rather than "Twenty-Two" as seen here.

Above, bottom: Caterpillar Twenty-Two pulling plow, 1935
Turning over the soil for another season, a Twenty-Two pulls a plow on a Midwestern farm. (Photograph © J. C. Allen & Son)

Left: 1930s Caterpillar Model Twenty-Two Orchard
A four-cylinder, overhead-valve engine with a bore and stroke of 4.00x5.00 inches (100x125 mm) powered the Twenty-Two Orchard.

Below: 1930s Caterpillar Model Twenty-Two Orchard
Looking more like a twenty-first-century moon rover than a tractor from the 1930s, this Twenty-Two bears the complete set of factory orchard accoutrements. Owner: Larry Maasdam.

Above: 1930s Caterpillar Model Twenty-Two Orchard
The Twenty-Two came in several variations, one of which was this orchard version. Larry Maasdam's Twenty-Two Orchard is unique among Caterpillars in that the master clutch lever is moved back to disengage. This is serial number 2F4200W; the "W" denotes its wide-tread stance.

Left: 1930s Caterpillar Model Twenty-Two Orchard
Oil pressure and water temperature were the only instruments on the panel of this orchard model. The control below the gauges was the selector for main or auxiliary fuel. The ignition switch was above the gauges.

By 1935, Caterpillar held the distinction of being the world's largest producer of diesels and the first to build the engines on a moving assembly line. The sale of tractors to the Soviet Union was a big factor in getting Caterpillar through the worst of the Great Depression, but the advent of the new diesel also contributed mightily.

The Diesel Models

The new Caterpillar Diesel (1C), as it was originally called, soon became the Diesel Sixty. It was a 24,390-pound (10,975-kg) version of the original Best Sixty. The Diesel pioneered the use of a two-cylinder gas auxiliary starting, or "pony," motor. The diesel engine had a bore and stroke of 6.125x9.25 inches (153.125x231.25 mm), displacing 1,090 ci (17,854 cc) and turning at 700 rpm. The fuel injection system was originally made by Robert Bosch, but Caterpillar later made its own.

A total of 157 of the Diesel Sixtys were delivered as serial numbers 1C1 through 1C157. Initially, sales were controlled by Caterpillar so that service help could be provided and records kept. Sales prospects willing to take a gamble on the new engine were not so numerous that Caterpillar could be choosy, however. Service men then began going with machines to many distant, exotic places, from Hawaii to Belgium.

By 1932, the Diesel Sixty had become the Diesel Sixty-Five, which only lasted in production until 1933. The engine was then put in a new chassis and it became the Diesel Seventy. The new chassis, including the transmission and running gear, were continued in production as the Diesel Seventy-Five and on into the D8 of 1954.

With the Diesel Seventy-Five (2E) of 1933 to 1935 came a new standard engine. Three-, four-, and six-cylinder versions of the engine were made, but each used the same 5.25x8.00-inch (131.25x200-mm) bore and stroke; the Diesel Seventy-Five used the six-cylinder variety. In

1935, the bore of the standard engine was increased to 5.75 inches (143.75 mm), and was mounted in the last thirty-five or so tractors, which used 5E serial numbers.

By 1936, Caterpillar chose to change its old spelled-out number designators. New models did not fit between the old numbers already used, and customers related the number designators to horsepower, which was no longer the case. When the competition offered a comparable model with higher advertised power than the Cat model number, a lot of explaining by Caterpillar salesmen was required.

In 1934, the U.S. government had purchased some special Caterpillar tractors for President Franklin Delano Roosevelt's New Deal construction projects. These special Caterpillar tractors required minor and major changes to be made to existing models. Some in Caterpillar management had no use for the New Deal and its make-work activities; therefore, these specials were given an "R" designation for "Roosevelt," followed by a single number. In 1936, when the model number problem became intolerable, it was decided to switch all models to this new

Caterpillar Twenty-Two Orchard, 1937

Working in a Michigan apple orchard, a Twenty-Two fitted with orchard fenders and a spray wagon in tow rests as a worker sprays a tree. (Photograph © J. C. Allen & Son)

Caterpillar Twenty-Two Orchard, 1936
A Twenty-Two with orchard fenders pulls a wagon stacked high with crates of freshly picked apples. (Photograph © J. C. Allen & Son)

Above: 1930s Caterpillar Model Twenty-Two Orchard

Owner Larry Maasdam aboard his Twenty-Two Orchard. Note the low seat typical of Cat orchard tractors.

Left: 1930s Caterpillar Model Twenty-Two Orchard

The fairing over the air intake of this Twenty-Two Orchard was part of the factory equipment to aid orchard workers in protecting their trees. Everything possible was done to allow the tractor to slip through the orchard with a minimum of damage.

1937 Caterpillar R2
The R2 E2 was much the same as the old "Flathead" Twenty, but with the overhead-valve engine of the Twenty-Two. Only 83 of the R2 E2 model were built for special U.S. government orders. This is serial number 5E 3570. Owner: Robert Stewart.

system, but in the case of the diesels, to add a "D" behind the "R." Accordingly, the Diesel Seventy-Five became the RD8 (1H). It was manufactured through 1938 with only minor improvements.

A series of smaller diesel-powered crawlers also came along in 1933, and each had a spark-ignition counterpart. The first was the Diesel Fifty (1E), which used the four-cylinder version of the original standard engine of 5.25x8.00-inch (131.25x200-mm) bore and stroke. The gas version was powered by a four-cylinder engine of 5.50x6.50 inches (137.50x162.50 mm). Both versions featured a four-speed transmission. Early versions of both had the fuel tank in front of the driver; later ones had the tank in the seatback. The gas version was discontinued in 1937, while the diesel became the RD7 (9G) in 1936.

Sold in 1933 and 1934, the Diesel Thirty-Five (6E) used the three-cylinder version of the standard engine rated at 850 rpm. Again, a four-speed gearbox was included. The gas Thirty-Five (5C) was the same except for the engine. Both had their roots in the old Best and

1937 Caterpillar R2
Robert Stewart's Caterpillar R2 is one of the last thirty built, and thus has the name "Caterpillar" above the radiator. Earlier R2 tractors had "R2" in that location.

Right, top: 1937 Caterpillar R2

The R2 was essentially the same as the Caterpillar Twenty-Two. Tractors using the R designator were slightly modified for special government orders. The Caterpillar R2 is essentially the same as the Twenty-Two, and both were produced together beginning in 1934. Production of the R2 ended in 1937, however, after only eighty-three were built. Production of the Twenty-Two continued through 1939. The R2 weighed in at about 6,000 pounds.

Right, bottom: 1939 Caterpillar R2

This later, 6J Series version of the R2 is not to be confused with the R2 5E. The 6J was the gasoline equivalent of the D2. Owner: Marv Fery.

Below: Caterpillar D2, 1936

A D2 diesel pulls a New Idea corn harvester and wagon through a bumper crop in a Midwestern field. (Photograph © J. C. Allen & Son)

Caterpillar Thirty models. The gas version used a four-cylinder engine of 4.875x6.50 inches (121.875x162.59 mm). The gas Thirty-Five was produced from 1932 to 1934.

The Diesel Forty (3G) came out in 1934. It was a modernized version of the Diesel Thirty-Five, making a break from the Best/Caterpillar Model Thirty heritage. Changes were mainly in the construction of the track frame. The standard three-cylinder engine was continued, with minor internal changes that gave a small power increase. The Diesel Forty became the RD6 (2H) in 1936 and was built as such through 1938. Introduced in 1934, the gas Forty (5G) used the improved track system and retained the engine of the gas Thirty-Five. Its production ended in 1936.

The 1936 RD4 (4G) was the diesel version of the new Caterpillar Thirty/R4 (6G). A new horizontally opposed two-cylinder starting motor was used. The RD4 was a 35-drawbar-hp machine. Early tractors differed from the newer in that two top rollers were used; newer versions, called simply the D4 after 1938, used only one.

The New Deal

While the 1930s began poorly for Caterpillar, 1932 was actually the only year the company lost money. By the time the decade was over, Caterpillar was offering a completely modernized line of tractors and graders, and it was miles ahead of the competition in diesels. Although some in Caterpillar management were not fans of President Roosevelt and his New Deal, the government make-work programs were good for the company and helped ensure profitability in subsequent years.

Left, top: 1930s Caterpillar R2
The R2 5E tractor was built only with a 50-inch-wide gauge. Made between 1934 and 1937, it was designed per U.S. government orders and was much the same tractor as the Model Twenty-Two, except the transmission gear ratios were different.

Left, center: 1930s Caterpillar R2
The R2 5E tractor was virtually the same as the Model Twenty-Two. They were produced at the same time, although only 83 R2s were made while more than 15,000 Twenty-Twos were turned out. This R2 was photographed at the Jenison-Meacham Memorial Art Center and Museum in Belmond, Iowa. Owner: Larry Maasdam.

Left, bottom: 1930s Caterpillar R2
This rare U.S. government-spec R2 had been owned since new by the U.S. Navy. Owner Larry Maasdam obtained it from a salvage yard in Fairfield, California. The R2 was in good condition when he found it, needing only new paint.

Roosevelt had created the New Deal to battle the Great Depression. To reduce unemployment and restore prosperity, Roosevelt and Congress endorsed a wide range of new federal programs and agencies, most popularly identified by acronym titles. Roosevelt won support for an unprecedented array of new services, regulations, and subsidies. An informal group of advisers known as the Brain Trust helped organize and push through the various programs. These individuals from outside government included professors, lawyers, and others who came to Washington to advise Roosevelt in these matters. Roosevelt and his Brain Trust employed a shotgun approach to the problems of the depression: They chose to do something, anything, even if it was the wrong thing. Indeed, many of their new ideas did not get past the U.S. Supreme Court.

Nevertheless, the New Deal helped get the economy going and aided farmers, and hence, tractor makers. The New Deal also sponsored vast construction projects, such as the Hoover Dam. Actually started during President Herbert Hoover's administration and named for him, it was renamed Boulder Dam by Roosevelt's Interior Secretary Harold Ickes, then again renamed Hoover Dam following World War II. Another project was the Tennessee Valley Authority (TVA), which built dams for flood control and rural electrification. The Grand Coulee Dam in Washington state was also erected during this period. In addition, the Civilian Conservation Corps (CCC) constructed roads and fire brakes and planted millions of seedling trees. Finally, the Works Progress Administration (WPA) built and maintained roads, airports, docks, and parks, and did other public works. All of these projects required large amounts of Caterpillar power.

Serving the Nation

World War II was the most devastating conflict in human history. It began in June 1939 as a dispute between Nazi Germany and an Anglo-French coalition concerned by German aggression in Poland and other countries. The conflict rapidly widened to include most of the nations of the world. The war ended in 1945, ushering in the Nuclear Age.

World War II had its roots in World War I, as both

1935 Caterpillar Twenty-Eight
The Twenty-Eight was an update of the Twenty-Five, more closely reflecting its true power capabilities. On the drawbar, the Twenty-Eight was rated at 30 hp. Owner: Marv Fery.

Above: 1932 Caterpillar Fifty

Model Fifty tractors up to serial number 5A757 had the fuel tank mounted in front of the driver; this 1932 version bears number 5A195. Later ones had the tank in the seat back. Owner Jerry Gast found this gasoline-powered machine abandoned in the woods where it had been severely vandalized. Earl Stalter of Caterpillar, Inc., helped Gast with drawings so that parts could be fabricated. Gast made the manifolds, choke assembly, front top carrier rollers, hood, and sprocket guards.

Left, top: 1932 Caterpillar Fifty

The gas Fifty had an unusual engine. It was of the cross-flow type with intake and exhaust manifolds on opposite sides. Individual cylinder heads and rocker covers were used.

Left, bottom: 1932 Caterpillar Fifty

The gas Fifty was not made in large numbers due to the popularity of diesels. Only about 1,800 were sold.

1930s Caterpillar Diesel brochure
This brochure offered "Reasons why farmers buy 'Caterpillar' Diesel."

the victors and the losers of the so-called War To End All Wars were dissatisfied. Germany bitterly resented its territorial losses and the imposed war reparations. Japan was on the winning side in World War I, but was unhappy about its failure to gain control of China. Italy was victorious, but embraced fascism rather than democracy, though democracy was decreed for all parties by the victors.

The United States emerged from World War II as the dominant superpower. It was one of the few combatants that suffered almost no damage to its home territory. America had almost all of the natural resources it needed within its home territory to press the war with vigor. It also possessed exceptional human and economic resources, along with superb industrial capability.

How American industry converted to the war effort in a short time and began producing armament at a record pace is a story of its own. Ford Motor Company, for example, broke ground for the construction of its mile-long

Willow Run airplane factory and airport in April 1941, and the first B-24 Liberator bomber flew out of the airport in July 1942. In two years and ten months, 8,685 of the four-engine bombers were delivered to the U.S. Army Air Corps. Production at the end of the war was running at a plane per hour. Virtually every American manufacturing company launched into building something they knew little about for the war effort and, despite obstacles, delivered quality products in record time. Caterpillar was no exception.

In January 1941, Congress passed the Lend-Lease Act, committing the United States to become an "Arsenal of Democracy," as President Roosevelt had declared. The Lend-Lease program harnessed American production capacity to assist the forces opposing Nazi Germany before the United States was officially involved. Items from bulldozers to airplanes were simply loaned or leased to the cash-strapped countries. Caterpillar soon committed a large part of its production of tractors, graders, genera-

"I Wanted Nothing But Diesel . . .
'Caterpillar' Is The Proven Diesel"
—Walter W. Hawk,
San Dimas, California

"When I bought a new tractor, I practically
didn't even look at competitive track-type
machines," states Walter W. Hawk, San
Dimas, California.

"I wasn't interested in anything but a Diesel,
and 'Caterpillar' has the only Diesel engine
that has been proven.

"So as far as I was concerned, 'Caterpillar'
was the only tractor on the market.

"I take care of about 285 acres of citrus with
my Diesel D2. Mostly contract. I used my
'Caterpillar' Twenty-Two on the same acreage.

"Many times with the Twenty-Two I had to
work far into the night. Now with the D2's
extra power and speed, I get most of my
work done in daylight."

• • •

"Caterpillar" Diesels are proven. "Caterpillar" has more than a decade of Diesel-
building experience. And behind these
Diesels is the satisfaction of scores of thousands of owners!

Left: 1930s Caterpillar Diesel brochure
D2 Orchard owner Walter W. Hawk of San Dimas, California, spoke out for Cat Diesels: "I wasn't interested in anything but a Diesel, and 'Caterpillar' has the only Diesel engine that has been proven."

Below: Caterpillar Diesel Sixty, 1931
The Best Sixty became the Caterpillar Sixty after the merger of 1925; this then became the Diesel Sixty when the new diesel engine was fitted in 1931.

tor sets, and other equipment to Lend-Lease.

When the United States entered the war in December 1941, Caterpillar immediately went on full wartime footing. Howitzer frames, 37-mm cannon shells, and tank transmissions were added to the list of items Cat produced for the war. Many Caterpillar products were discontinued during the war years to make room for the production of D7 and D8 tractors. D7 bulldozers were favored by the military because they fit neatly in small landing craft. In fact, demand for the D7 became so great that the U.S. Government also ordered American Car and Foundry of Berwick, Pennsylvania, to build more than 1,000 D7s, which were denoted by 4T serial number prefixes. As in many other plants, Cat scheduled three shifts of workers six days per week. Many employees volunteered for an extra four-hour "Victory Shift." Vacations were suspended. New employees—mostly women untrained in factory work—replaced thousands of men who went on military leave.

Caterpillar equipment served on every front, from the Arctic to Africa, Europe to the Pacific. In the process, Cat earned a reputation for dependability. The author's uncle, Norman E. Pripps, eighty-nine years old at this writing, remembers that his U.S. Navy Seabee battalion had bulldozers of all the various brands. They kept the Caterpillar D8s throughout the war; crawlers from other brands were junked on each Pacific Island that was invaded.

Caterpillar Tank Engines

The Wright R-1820 Cyclone aircraft engine came out in 1930 and stayed in production for the next twenty-five years. It was an air-cooled, four-stroke, nine-cylinder radial engine with a bore and stroke of 6.10x6.90 inches (152.50x172.50 mm), displacing 1,820 ci (29,812 cc). Weight was about 1,000 pounds (450 kg). By the mid-1930s, it had been developed to produce 1,200 hp at 2,200 rpm; by the end of its production, it was rated at 1,525 hp. The Cyclone was a successful and highly respected

Caterpillar Diesel Sixty, 1930s
The Diesel Sixty became popular in the logging industry as the diesel version used about half as much fuel as the gasoline version. (Smithsonian Institution)

1934 Caterpillar Diesel Seventy-Five

This sixty-five-year-old tractor looks ready to go to work. Serial number 2E46, it spent its early life farming in Northern California. In 1934, it sold for $4,300.

1934 Caterpillar Diesel Seventy-Five

The Diesel Seventy-Five was made from 1933 to 1935, and boasted 93 hp from its 5.25x8.00-inch (131.25x200-mm), six-cylinder engine. Owner: Larry Simon.

engine that was used on the Douglas DC-2 and was optional on the DC-3. Its last applications were in the post-war North American T-28 Trojan and the Grumman S2F Tracker.

In the late 1930s, Wright was asked by the U.S. Army to adapt the R-1820 engine to power the Sherman and other tanks. There were several reasons the army chose an aircraft engine for a tank. At the time, only aircraft engines were made with an adequate power-to-weight ratio. Although tanks were heavy, weight was a serious concern, since every pound affects performance and fuel consumption. Air-cooled engines were preferred for tanks because of the vulnerability of coolant-filled radiators.

Wright's tank engine was designated the G-200A. In most applications, power was derated to about 500 hp. With the addition of a cooling fan and output drive, the G-200A came in at about 1,350 pounds (608 kg).

Fuel consumption was a problem, however, as the G-

200A could go through 30 gallons (114 liters) of gas every hour when working hard. Space limitations for fuel inside the tank meant that the tank's range was limited. Also, with gas weighing 6 pounds per gallon (2.7 kg per liter), the army became interested in what a heavier, but not so thirsty, diesel could do for them. And who knew more about diesels than Caterpillar?

In July 1941, Caterpillar engineers began the task of converting the G-200A to run not only on diesel fuel, but on other fuels as well. The engine was designated the D-200A. In November 1942, authorization was given for 450-hp D-200A engines to be installed in twenty Sherman M4A4 tanks. Tests were successful, although there was some difficulty with piston scoring when using gas; adding oil to the gas alleviated this problem.

In January 1943, 1,000 engines were ordered. Caterpillar formed a subsidiary, Caterpillar Military Engine Company, to manufacture the engine in Decatur, Illinois.

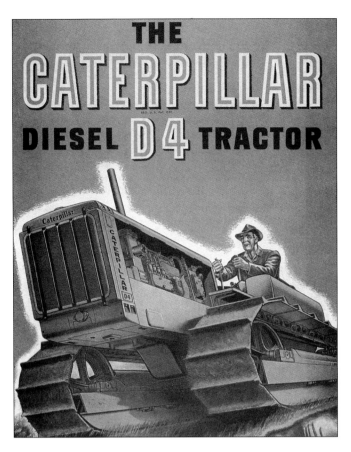

1940s Caterpillar D4 brochure

The engine designation was changed to RD-1820, and 775 more were ordered. Delivery of the tanks began in October 1943, but in February 1944, after only seventy-five tanks were delivered, the program was cancelled. The reasons given by the army involved the difficulty of supplying troops with two kinds of fuel. If diesel fuel was not used in the RD-1820, many of its benefits were lost. Also, the RD-1820 was longer than the gas version and would only fit in lengthened tanks—and it was almost three times heavier.

The Alaska Highway

When France fell before the Nazi juggernaut in June 1940, Americans began to take the war seriously. A Canadian and American "Permanent Joint Board of Defense" was established. Defense of Alaska, Western Canada, and the West Coast of the United States was considered. At the time, there was no land route from the contiguous United States through Western Canada to Alaska. Roads suitable for truck traffic did not continue past Dawson Creek, British Columbia.

In 1941, six airfields were constructed in Western Canada, called Northwest Staging Route Fields, allowing shorter-range airplane flights from the United States to

Caterpillar RD4, 1937
An RD4 pulls a plow to break the spring soil. (Photograph © J. C. Allen & Son)

1935 Caterpillar Diesel Forty
This Diesel Forty was purchased new in 1935 by Woodland Township, Wright County, Minnesota, and was used for snowplowing by the township until 1965. When there was no snow on the ground, the Forty pulled a grader. Owner: Woodland Township.

Ladd Field in Fairbanks, Alaska. With completion of the airfields, fighter planes were flown to Fairbanks, where Soviet pilots picked them up as part of the Lend-Lease Act.

When the United States and Japan went to war in December 1941, near-panic set in over the possibility of a Japanese attack in Alaska and the lack of adequate defenses there. In February 1942, Roosevelt authorized work to begin on what was then called the Alcan Highway, a construction project second in scope only to the building of the Panama Canal. The route chosen would connect Dawson Creek, British Columbia, to Fairbanks, Alaska, and all of the Northwest Staging Route Fields between. The Canadians provided the land, gravel, and timber, while the work was done and financed through the U.S. Army.

The first train carrying construction crews and equipment arrived in Dawson Creek on March 2, 1942. Soon, some 10,000 Corps of Engineer troops and 6,000 civilian construction workers were at work on the 1,400-mile (2,240-km) project that traversed 1,200 miles (1,920 km) in Canada and 200 miles (320 km) in Alaska. The crews were equipped with thousands of bulldozers and road graders, 70 percent of which were Caterpillars. Pressing through unbelievably difficult terrain, through mud that sometimes was as high as the top crawler rollers, through

Caterpillar Collector Profile: Larry Simon

Larry Simon has been around heavy equipment since he was fourteen years old. Today he runs a 690 backhoe and a Grade-All for the highway department of Blackhawk County, Iowa. Simon and his wife Diana, and their children Rachael and Michael, live on an acreage near Waterloo, Iowa. Simon's neighbor is Cat collector Kevin Kalsem.

During his years in the construction industry, Simon worked as both a mechanic and operator. Today, he has about twenty-five Caterpillars in various stages of repair. He's also a collector of old Cat literature.

clouds of mosquitoes and black flies, the "Pioneer Road" was completed at the rate of 8 miles (12.8 km) per day. In a little over six months, a 24-foot-wide (7.2-meter) roadway and 200 bridges were constructed. D8 bulldozers following a blaze line left by the surveyors cleared most of the initial roadway. Often, the D8s caught up to the surveyors.

Once the Pioneer Road was cut through, civilian contractors undertook the tasks of widening the roadbed for two-way traffic, improving the grades, and replacing temporary bridges. The first convoy of trucks arrived in Fairbanks in late November 1942.

1940s Caterpillar D4
A D4 pulls a Deere Killefer hydraulic plow through a California field.

Above: 1935 Caterpillar Diesel Forty

Woodland Township's Diesel Forty was restored through the combined efforts of several Cat aficionados. Collector-restorer Ed Claessen rebuilt the cab and donated components to the restoration. The local Ziegler Caterpillar dealership in Minnesota repainted the machine.

Right: 1935 Caterpillar Diesel Forty

The Diesel Thirty-Five and Diesel Forty shared basic engines, but while the Thirty-Five was rated at 44 drawbar hp, the Forty was a 55-drawbar-hp tractor. The three-cylinder Diesel Forty became the RD6 in 1936 when designations on all Cats were changed.

Above: Caterpillar Diesel Forty, 1934
A Diesel Forty pulls a plow to prepare the soil for planting.

Left: 1935 Caterpillar Diesel Forty
The Diesel Forty had a side-by-side, two-cylinder, side-valve starting motor. The pistons go in opposite directions, as on a John Deere two-cylinder engine.

1935 Caterpillar Diesel Forty
The Diesel Forty was made between 1934 and 1936.

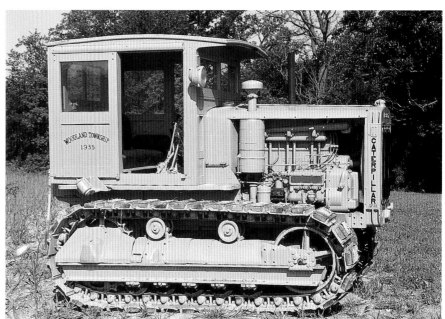

1935 Caterpillar Diesel Forty
Woodland Township's 1935 Diesel Forty has street-pad tracks. The township also has a V-style snowplow with wings for this venerable crawler.

1934 Caterpillar Diesel Forty
Tested by the University of Nebraska in 1935, the Diesel Forty tipped the scales at 15,642 pounds (7,039 kg).

Right: 1934 Caterpillar Diesel Forty
The left side of the Diesel Forty's three-cylinder engine.

Below left: 1934 Caterpillar Diesel Forty
The controls of the Diesel Forty.

Below right: 1934 Caterpillar Diesel Forty
Collector Alan Smith maneuvers his restored Diesel Forty.

1934 Caterpillar Diesel Forty

This Diesel Forty, serial number 3G1603 SP, has the wide-gauge option. The Diesel Forty was fairly rare, but was known for the long life of its three-cylinder engine. Owner: Alan Smith.

1934 Caterpillar Diesel Forty
The engine was a three-cylinder version of the standard 5.25x8.00-inch (131.25x200-mm) powerplant.

1934 Caterpillar Diesel Forty
The Diesel Forty was an upgraded version of the Diesel Thirty-Five, which was sold in 1933 and 1934.

Caterpillar RD6, 1937
An RD6 pulls a combine through California wheatfields. The RD6 used a 55-hp, three-cylinder engine. (Eastman Collection, University of California–Davis)

Caterpillar RD6, 1936
While the driver looks worn out by hours working the fields, his RD6 pulls its duet of plows without complaint. (Photograph © J. C. Allen & Son)

Above: Caterpillar D6, 1940s
A rare early color photograph of a D6 at work in the 1940s.

Left: 1940s Caterpillar D6 bro-chure

1930s Caterpillar Diesel Fifty
Early versions of the Diesel Fifty had the fuel tank in front of the driver. Later editions, such as the one shown here, had the tank in the seat back. Owner: Robert Stewart.

1930s Caterpillar Diesel brochure

Caterpillar Collector Profile: Robert Stewart

Robert Stewart Sr. has been in the excavating business for about thirty years. Robert Stewart Jr., Caterpillar collector, is also in the business. Their firm, Robert Stewart Excavating, is located in Fontana, Wisconsin. They operate two track loaders, a 943 and 953B; a 320L excavator; a 936F wheel loader; D6D and D3LGP dozers; and four big Mack dump trucks. The business's garage holds Stewart Sr.'s restored 1926 AC Mack chain-drive dump truck.

Stewart Jr. and his wife Lisa's place in the country houses a variety of collectibles besides the Caterpillar equipment. One interesting piece is the engine, radiator, and transmission of a JT crawler. Stewart found it in Butternut, Wisconsin, where it was being used at a sawmill powerplant. This may be the very JT that the author's grandfather bought new in 1918. The JT was donated for scrap during World War II, but it's likely that some unpatriotic scrap dealer decided to make a few bucks and sold the engine to the sawmill owner.

1930s Caterpillar Diesel Fifty
Essentially the same tractor as the gas Fifty, the Diesel Fifty was fitted with a four-cylinder version of the 5.25x8.00-inch (131.25x200-mm) standard engine. The last twenty-five built, however, had the bore increased to 5.75 inches (143.75 mm).

Above: 1936 Caterpillar RD8

Larry Maasdam's RD8 is in fine operating condition, but has not yet received cosmetic treatment. The RD8 was a big machine, weighing almost 34,000 pounds (15,300 kg).

Left: 1936 Caterpillar RD8

The RD8 was "big iron" in its day, as it featured a six-cylinder engine of 103 hp. The Diesel Seventy-Five became the RD8 in 1936, and the "RD" designation was carried through 1938; the designation was simply "D8" thereafter. Owner: Larry Maasdam.

1930s Caterpillar Sixty-Five
The gas Sixty-Five was quite rare, with only 521 built. This venerable machine was used for crushing junk cars for decades in Chico, Minnesota. Owner: Larry Simon.

Caterpillar D2 hauling logs, 1936
This was quite a load, especially for a D2. The machine was working in the forests of Northern California. (Eastman Collection, University of California–Davis)

Above: Caterpillar D7 in London, 1940
Caterpillars served on all fronts in World War II. Here, a miserable-looking British soldier clears bomb damage from the street.

Right: 1940s Caterpillar wartime factory poster
This poster was displayed in Caterpillar plants during World War II. All Cat factories were on wartime footing, with women and older men replacing those men that had gone into the military.

Above: Caterpillar D4 at war, 1940s
Fitted with armor plating, a D4 advances with troops during the World War II Solomon Island campaign.

Left: 1940s Caterpillar wartime advertisement
"As fast as troops can march," promised this Caterpillar ad, which promoted Cat's contributions to the war effort, from the use of crawlers to build the Alcan Highway to machines serving with the U.S. Army Corps of Engineers in North Africa.

Caterpillar D8 building the Alcan Highway, 1942
U.S. Army troops widen a stretch of the road with the help of a D8. To build the Alcan, some 10,000 Corps of Engineer soldiers worked alongside 6,000 civilians. (Courtesy Pictorial Histories Publishing)

Caterpillar D8 grading roadbed on the Alcan Highway, 1942
Stretches of road on higher ground were built quickly by the troops punching through the 1942 pioneer road. (Courtesy Pictorial Histories Publishing)

Caterpillar D8s at work on the Alcan Highway, 1943
The pioneer road was cut through in the winter of 1942. Here, D8s working for the Utah Construction Company improved the initial road at Goose Bay on Tulane Lake. The Utah Construction Company was a private contractor working for the army. (National Archives; courtesy Pictorial Histories Publishing)

Above: Caterpillar Fifty leads the way on the Alcan Highway, 1943

A 40-mile (64-km) section of the Alcan Highway from Pickhandle Lake to Beaver Creek became a great bottleneck in spring 1943 as convoys of trucks had to be pulled through the section. Here, a fleet of Studebaker-built 6x6s get a pull from a gas Fifty. (National Archives; courtesy Pictorial Histories Publishing)

Left: Caterpillar D8 ferries equipment on the Alcan Highway, 1942

A D8 serves on ferry duty, pulling troops and equipment through another of the prodigious patches of mud. (U.S. Army; courtesy Pictorial Histories Publishing)

Above: Caterpillar D8 covers culvert on the Alcan Highway, 1942

The use of wooden culverts was accepted practice when making the pioneer road in 1942. These were later replaced or bypassed when the permanent road was completed. This D8 seems to have taken quite a beating. (National Archives; courtesy Pictorial Histories Publishing)

Right: Caterpillar D8 rescue mission on the Alcan Highway, 1943

Members of the Ninety-seventh Engineers hitch up a D8 to rescue another D8 that was bogged down in mud. (U.S. Army; courtesy Pictorial Histories Publishing)

1930s Caterpillar Diesel Fifty
The Diesel Fifty came out in 1933 and production continued through 1936. Don Kagel operates Robert Stewart's Diesel Fifty, serial number 1E1784.

Alexander Botts and the Earthworm Tractor

Tractor salesman extraordinaire Alexander Botts was created by writer William Hazlett Upson for a story entitled "I'm a Natural Born Salesman" that first appeared in the *Saturday Evening Post* on April 16, 1927. Botts sold the fictitious Earthworm crawler tractors, made by the Farmers' Friend Tractor Company of Earthworm City, Illinois. The Earthworm was based on the Caterpillar, but Botts was a true original.

Botts sprung from Upson's own experience working in the Holt Caterpillar service department from 1919 to 1924. "I spent a lot of time traveling around the country shooting trouble, repairing tractors, and instructing the operators," Upson wrote about his time with Holt. "My main job was to follow up the salesmen and try to make the tractors do what the salesmen had said they would. In this way I came to know more about salesmen than they know about themselves."

In the 1950s, Upson offered the following

biography of his hero: "Alexander Botts was born in Smedleytown, Iowa, on March 15, 1892, the son of a prosperous farmer. He finished high school there; then embarked on a series of jobs—none of them quite worthy of his mettle. In these early days the largest piece of machinery he sold was the Excelsior Peerless Self-Adjusting Safety Razor Blade Sharpener. He became interested in heavy machinery in 1918 while serving in France as a cook with the motorized field artillery. In March, 1920, he was hired as a salesman by the Farmers' Friend Tractor Company, which later became the Earthworm Tractor Company.

"On April 12, 1926, he met Miss Mildred Deane, the attractive daughter of an Earthworm dealer in Mercedillo, California. Seven days later they were married. Mildred, later nicknamed Gadget, had attended the language schools at Middlebury College (Vermont) and acted as interpreter for her husband when he was sent to Europe in 1928 to open new tractor outlets there.

"Mr. And Mrs. Botts returned from Europe in early 1929 to await the birth of Alexander Botts, Jr., who arrived in February along with a twin sister, Little Gadget."

Upson's stories about Botts and the Earthworm became so popular that he continued the series for decades, eventually penning 112 Botts tales between 1927 and 1975.

In 1936, Hollywood immortalized the salesman in the movie *Earthworm Tractors,* with comedian actor Joe E. Brown starring as Botts. In the movie, Botts struggles to sell a stubborn prospect on the merits of the crawlers while at the same time hoping to win his daughter's hand. The movie crew took over the Caterpillar plant for several weeks to make the film, and when the movie made its debut, it was first shown, fittingly enough, in Peoria.

Here is the first installment of Botts's adventures selling Earthworms.

Alexander Botts—Earthworm Tractors collection, 1929

I'm a Natural Born Salesman

By William Hazlett Upson

STONEWALL JACKSON HOTEL
MEMPHIS, TENNESSEE

March 15, 1920.

The Farmers' Friend Tractor Company,
Earthworm City, Ill.

GENTLEMEN: I have decided you are the best tractor company in the country, and consequently I am giving you first chance to hire me as your salesman to sell tractors in this region.

I'm a natural born salesman, have a very quick mind, am twenty-eight years old, am honest and reliable, and can give references if required. I have already had considerable experience as a machinery salesman, and I became familiar with your Earthworm tractors as a member of the motorized field artillery in France. I can demonstrate tractors as well as sell them.

When do I start work?

Very truly yours,

ALEXANDER BOTTS.

FARMERS' FRIEND TRACTOR COMPANY
MAKERS OF EARTHWORM TRACTORS
EARTHWORM CITY, ILLINOIS

March 17, 1920.

Mr. Alexander Botts,
Stonewall Jackson Hotel,
Memphis, Tenn.

DEAR MR. BOTTS: Your letter is received. We have no opening for a salesman at present, but we are badly in need of a service mechanic. As you say you are familiar with our tractors, we will try you out on this job, at $100 per month plus traveling expenses.

You will report at once to our Mr. George Healy, salesman for Tennessee and Mississippi, who is now at the Dartmouth Hotel, Memphis.

You will go with him to Cyprus City, Mississippi, to demonstrate a ten ton Earthworm tractor for Mr. Jackson, a lumber operator of that place. Mr. Healy will tell you just what you are to do.

We enclose check for $100 advance expense money.

Very truly,

GILBERT HENDERSON,
Sales Manager.

STONEWALL JACKSON HOTEL
MEMPHIS, TENNESSEE

March 19, 1920.

The Farmers' Friend Tractor Company,
Earthworm City, Ill.

GENTLEMEN: As soon as your letter came, I went around to see Mr. Healy, and it is lucky for you that you hired me, because Mr. Healy has just been taken sick with appendicitis. They were getting ready to take him to the hospital, and he was pretty weak, but he managed to tell me that the tractor for the demonstration had already arrived at the freight station in Cyprus City.

He also explained that this Mr. Jackson down there owns about a million feet of Cyprus timber which he wants to get out and sell right away before the present high price of lumber goes down. It seems the ground is so swampy and soft from the winter rains that with his present equipment of mules and wagons he won't be able to move any of his timber until summer.

But Mr. Healy was down there a couple of weeks ago, and he arranged to put on a demonstration to show Mr. Jackson that an Earthworm tractor can go into those swamps and drag out the timber right away. Mr. Jackson said he would buy the tractor if it did the work, and Mr. Healy was feeling very low because he was sick and couldn't go down to hold the demonstration.

"You can rest easy, Mr. Healy," I said. "When you look at me you're gazing on a natural born salesman. I will go down there and do your work as well as mine. I will put on a swell demonstration, and then I will sell the goods."

As Mr. Healy did not seem to know just what to say to this, I gathered up all his order blanks, selling literature, price lists, etc., and also the bill of lading and the check to pay the freight on the tractor. Then I wished him good luck, and left.

From this you can see that I am quick to grasp an opportunity, and that you made no mistake in hiring me. I am leaving for Cyprus City tonight.

Cordially yours,

ALEXANDER BOTTS.

FARMERS' FRIEND TRACTOR COMPANY
SALESMAN'S DAILY REPORT
Date: March 20, 1920.
Written from: Delta Hotel, Cyprus City, Miss.
Written by: Alexander Botts, Service Mechanic and Pinch Hitter Salesman.

I found this pad of salesman's report blanks among the stuff I got from Mr. Healy. I see by the instructions on the cover that each salesman is supposed to send in a full and complete report of everything he does, so I will give you all particulars of a very busy day.

I arrived at 7:51 this morning at Cyprus City—which turns out to be pretty much of a hick town in what they call the Yazoo Delta. The whole country here is nothing but a swamp, and the main street of the town ends in a high bank that they call a levee, on the other side of which is the Mississippi River flowing along about twenty feet higher than the town.

After alighting from the train, and after noting that it was a cloudy day and looked like rain, I engaged a room at the Delta Hotel. I then hurried over to the freight station where I found the big ten ton Earthworm tractor on the unloading platform. They had dragged it off the car with a block and tackle. And when I saw that beautiful machine standing there so big and powerful, with its fine wide tracks like an army tank, with its

elegant new shiny paint, and with its stylish cab for the driver, I will admit that I felt a glow of pride to think that I was the salesman and service mechanic for such a splendid piece of machinery.

(NOTE: Of course, as I said in my letter, I am an old machinery salesman. But the largest thing I ever sold before was the Excelsior Peerless Self-adjusting Automatic Safety Razor Blade Sharpener. I did very well with this machine, but I could not take the pride in it that I feel I am going to have in this wonderful ten ton Earthworm tractor.)

After paying the freight, I hired several guys from the town garage to put gas and oil in the tractor, and then I started them bolting the little cleats onto the tracks. You see I am right up on my toes all the time. I think of everything. And I figured that if we were going through the mud we would need these cleats to prevent slipping. While they were being put on, I stepped over to the office of Mr. Johnson, the lumber man.

(NOTE: This bird's name is Johnson—not Jackson, as you and Mr. Healy told me. Also it strikes me that Mr. Healy may have been fairly sick even as long as two weeks ago when he was down here. In addition to getting the name wrong, he did very poor work in preparing this prospect. He did not seem to be in a buying mood at all.)

As soon as I had explained my errand to this Mr. Johnson—who is a very large, hard-boiled bozo—he gave me what you might call a horse laugh. "You are wasting your time," he said. "I told that fool salesman who was here before that tractors would be no good to me. All my timber is four miles away on the other side of the Great Gumbo Swamp, which means that it would have to be brought through mud that is deeper and stickier that anything you ever seen, young feller."

"You would like to get it out, wouldn't you?" I asked.

"I sure would," he said, "but it's impossible. You don't understand conditions down here. Right on the roads the mules and horses sink in up to their bellies; and when you get off the roads, even ducks and turtles can hardly navigate."

"The Earthworm tractor," I said, "has more power than any duck or turtle. And if you'll come out with me, I'll show you that I can pull your logs through that swamp."

"I can't afford to waste my time with such crazy ideas," he said. "I've tried motor equipment. I have a motor truck now that is stuck three feet deep right on the main road at the edge of town."

"All right," I said, always quick to grasp an opportunity, "how about coming along with me while I pull out your truck?"

"Well," said Mr. Johnson, "I can spare about an hour this morning. If you'll go right now, I'll go with you—although I doubt if you can even pull out the truck. And even if you do, I won't buy your tractor."

"How about going this afternoon?" I asked.

"I'll be busy this afternoon. It's now or never."

"Come on!" I said.

We went over to the freight platform, and as the cleats were now all bolted on we both climbed into the cab.

(NOTE: I will explain that I was sorry that Mr. Johnson had been unable to wait until afternoon, as I had intended to use the morning in practicing up on driving the machine. It is true, as I said in my letter, that I became familiar with Earthworm tractors when I was a member of a motorized artillery outfit in France, but as my job in the artillery was that of cook, and as I had never before sat in the seat of one of these tractors, I was not as familiar with the details of driving as I might have wished. However, I was pleased to see that the tractor seemed to have a clutch and gear shift like the automobiles I have often driven, and a pair of handle bars for steering very much like those of a tricycle I had operated in my early boyhood.)

I sat down on the driver's seat with reasonable confidence; Mr. Johnson sat down beside me; and one of the garage men cranked up the motor. It started at once, and when I heard the splendid roar of the powerful exhaust, and saw that thirty or forty of the inhabitants, both white and otherwise, were standing around with wondering and admiring faces, I can tell you I felt proud of myself. I put the gear in low, opened the throttle, and let in the clutch.

(NOTE: I would suggest that you tell your chief

engineer, or whoever it is that designs your tractors, that he ought to put in a standard gear shift. You can understand that it is very annoying—after you have pulled the gear shift lever to the left and then back—to find that instead of being in low you are really in reverse.)

As I said, I opened the throttle, let in the clutch, and started forward. But I found that when I started forward, I was really—on account of the funny gear shift—moving backwards. And instead of going down the gentle slope of the ramp in front, the whole works backed off the rear edge of the platform, dropping at least four feet into a pile of crates with such a sickening crash that I thought the machine was wrecked and both of us killed.

But it soon appeared that, although we were both very much shaken up, we were still alive—especially Mr. Johnson, who began talking so loud and vigorously that I saw I need have no worry about his health. After I had got Mr. Johnson quieted down a bit, I inspected the machine and found that it was not hurt at all. As I am always alert to seize an opportunity, I told Mr. Johnson that I had run off the platform on purpose to show him how strongly built the tractor was. Then, after I had promised I would not make any more of these jumps, he consented to remain in the tractor, and we started off again

(NOTE: Kindly tell your chief engineer that Alexander Botts congratulates him on producing a practically unbreakable tractor. But tell him that I wish he would design some thicker and softer seat cushions. If the base of the chief engineer's spine was as sore as mine still is, he would realize that there are times when good thick seat cushions are highly desirable.)

As we drove up the main street of Cyprus City, with a large crowd of admiring natives following after, I seemed to smell something burning. At once I stopped, opened up the hood, and discovered that the paint on the cylinders was crackling and smoking like bacon in a frying pan.

"Perhaps," suggested Mr. Johnson, "there is no water in the radiator."

I promptly inspected the radiator, and, sure enough, that was the trouble.

(NOTE: I would suggest that if your chief

engineer would design an air-cooled motor for the tractor, such incidents as the above would be avoided.)

I borrowed a pail from a store, and filled the radiator. Apparently, owing to my alertness in this emergency, no damage had been done.

When we started up again, we had not gone more than a few yards before I felt the tractor give a little lurch. After we had got a little farther along I looked back, and right at the side of the street I saw one of the biggest fountains I have ever seen in all my life. A solid column of water about eight inches thick was spouting high in the air, spreading out at the top like a mushroom, and raining down all around like Niagara Falls.

I heard somebody yell something about a fire plug; and, as I have a quick mind, I saw right away what had happened. The hood of the tractor is so big that it had prevented me from seeing a fire plug right in front of me. I had unfortunately run right into it, and as it was of very cheap, inferior construction, it had broken right off.

For a while there was great excitement, with people running here and there, hollering and yelling. The sheriff came up and took my name, as he seemed to think I was to blame—in spite of the fact that the fire plug was in such an exposed position. I was a bit worried at the way the water was accumulating in the street, and consequently I was much relieved when they finally got hold of the water works authorities and got the water turned off. You see the fire mains here are connected to the Mississippi River, and if they had not turned the water off the whole river would have flowed into the business district of Cyprus City.

(NOTE: I would suggest that your chief engineer design these tractor hoods a little lower so as to avoid such accidents in the future.)

After the water had been turned off, we got under way again, clanking along the main street in high gear, and then driving out of town to the eastward over one of the muddiest roads I ever saw. The tractor, on account of its wide tracks, stayed right up on top of the mud, and rolled along as easy and smooth as a Pullman car. Behind us a large crowd of local sightseers floundered along as best they could—some of them wading through the mud and slop, and others riding in buggies pulled by horses or mules.

Mr. Johnson acted as if he was pretty sore—and I did not blame him. Although the various mishaps and accidents we had been through were unavoidable and not my fault at all, I could understand that they might have been very annoying to my passenger. Perhaps that is one reason I am such a good salesman; I can always get the other fellow's point of view. I livened up the journey a bit by telling Mr. Johnson a number of Irish jokes, but I did not seem to get any laughs—possibly because the motor made so much noise Mr. Johnson couldn't hear me.

By this time I had got the hang of driving the machine very well, and I was going along like a veteran. When we reached Mr. Johnson's truck—which was deep in the mud at the side of the road about a half mile from town—I swung around and backed up in front of it in great style.

The road, as I have said, was soft and muddy enough but off to the right was a low, flat stretch of swamp land that looked much muddier, and a whole lot softer. There were patches of standing water here and there, and most of it was covered with canebrake—which is a growth of tall canes that look like bamboo fishing poles.

Mr. Johnson pointed out over this mass of canebrake and mud. "That is an arm of the Great Gumbo Swamp," he yelled very loud so I could hear him above the noise of the motor. "Your machine may be able to navigate these roads, but it would never pull a load through a slough like that."

I rather doubted it myself, but I didn't admit it. "First of all," I said, "we'll pull out this truck."

We both got out of the tractor, and right away we sank up to our knees in the soft sticky mud. The truck was a big one, loaded with lumber, and it was mired down so deep that the wheels were practically out of sight, and the body seemed to be resting on the ground. Mr. Johnson didn't think the tractor could budge it, but I told him to get into the driver's seat of the truck so he could steer it when it got going.

By this time a gentle rain had started up, and Mr. Johnson told me to hurry up as the truck had no cab and he was getting wet. I grabbed a big chain out of the truck tool box, and told Mr. Johnson to get out his watch. He did so.

"In just thirty seconds," I said, "things are going to start moving around here."

I then rapidly hooked one end of the chain to the back of the tractor, fastened the other end to the truck, sprang into the tractor seat, and started the splendid machine moving forward. As the tractor rolled steadily and powerfully down the road, I could hear the shouting of the crowd even above the noise of the motor. Looking around, however, I saw that something was wrong. The truck—or rather, the major portion of it—was still in the same place, and I was pulling only the radiator. As I had a quick mind, I saw at once what had happened. Quite naturally, I had slung the chain around the handiest thing on the front of the truck—which happened to be the radiator cap. And as the truck was of a cheap make, with the radiator not properly anchored, it had come off.

I stopped at once, and then I had to spend about ten minutes calming down Mr. Johnson by assuring him that the Farmers' Friend Tractor Company would pay for a new radiator. I backed up to the truck again, and Mr. Johnson took the chain himself, and by burrowing down in the mud managed to get it fastened around the front axle. Then he climbed back into the seat of the truck and scowled at me very disagreeably. By this time the rain was falling fairly briskly, and this may have had something to do with his ill humor.

When I started up again, everything went well. The motor roared, the cleats on the tracks dug into the mud and slowly and majestically the tractor moved down the road, dragging the heavy truck through the mud behind it.

At this point I stuck my head out of the tractor cab to acknowledge the cheers of the bystanders, and in so doing I unfortunately knocked off my hat, which was caught by the wind and blown some distance away. At once I jumped out and began chasing it through the mud. The crowd began to shout and yell, but I paid no attention to this noise until I had

reached my hat and picked it up—which took me some time, as the hat had blown a good ways, and I could not make any speed through the mud. When at last I looked around, I saw that a very curious thing had happened.

In getting out of the tractor I had accidentally pulled on one of the handle bars enough to turn the tractor sidewise. And in my natural excitement—the hat having cost me $8.98 last week in Memphis—I had forgotten to pull out the clutch. So when I looked up, I saw that the tractor with Mr. Johnson and his truck in tow, was headed right out into the Great Gumbo Swamp. It had already got a good start, and it was going strong. As Mr. Johnson seemed to be waving and yelling for help, I ran after him. But as soon as I got off the road the mud was so deep and soft that I could make no headway at all. Several of the bystanders also attempted to follow, but had to give it up as a bad job. There was nothing to do but let poor Mr. Johnson go dragging off through the swamp.

And, although I was really sorry to see it, Mr. Johnson going off all by himself this way, with no protection from the pouring rain, I could not help feeling a thrill of pride when I saw how the great ten ton Earthworm tractor was eating up that terrible soft mud. The wide tracks kept it from sinking in more than a few inches; the cleats gave it good traction; and the motor was so powerful that it pulled that big truck like it was a mere matchbox—and this in spite of the fact that the truck sank in so deep that it plowed a regular ditch as it went along.

As I am a natural born salesman, and quick to grasp every opportunity, I yelled a little sales talk after Mr. Johnson. "It's all right," I hollered; "I'm doing this on purpose to show you that the Earthworm can go through any swamp you got." But I doubt if he heard me; the roar of the tractor motor was too loud. And a moment later the tractor, the truck, and Mr. Johnson had disappeared in the canebrake.

While I was considering what to do next, a nice looking man in a corduroy suit came over to me from one of the groups of bystanders. "This is only an arm of the Great Gumbo Swamp," he said. "If that tractor doesn't mire down, and if it goes straight, it will come out on the levee on the other side about a mile from here."

"An Earthworm tractor never mires down," I said. "And as long as there is nobody there to pull on the handlebars, it can't help going straight."

"All right," said the man, "if you want to hop in my buggy, I'll drive you back to town and out the levee so we can meet it when it gets there."

"Fine!" I said. "Let's go." I have always been noted for my quick decisions, being similar to Napoleon in this particular. I at once climbed in the buggy with the man in the corduroy suit, and he drove the horse as fast as possible into town and then out the levee, with all the sightseers plowing along behind—both on foot and in buggies.

When we reached the place where the tractor ought to come out, we stopped and listened. Far out in the swamp we could hear the roar of the tractor motor. It got gradually louder and louder. We waited. It was still raining hard. Suddenly there was a shout from the crowd. The tractor came nosing out of the canebrake, and a moment later it had reached the bottom of the levee, with the big truck and Mr. Johnson dragging along behind. As the tractor was in low gear, I had no trouble in jumping aboard and stopping it—and it is just as well I was there to do this. If I had not stopped it, it would have shot right on over the levee and into the Mississippi River, probably drowning poor Mr. Johnson.

As it was, Mr. Johnson was as wet as a sponge, on account of the heavy rain, and because he had been too cheap to get himself a truck with a cab on it. But he was a long way from being drowned. In fact, he seemed very lively; and as I got down from the tractor he jumped out of the truck and came running at me, waving his arms around, and shouting and yelling, and with a very dirty look on his face. What he had to say to me would fill a small book; in fact, he said so much that I'm afraid I will have to put off telling you about it until my report tomorrow.

It is now midnight and I am very tired, so I will merely enclose my expense account for the day and wish you a pleasant good night. Kindly send check to cover expenses as soon as possible. As you will see, my $100 advance is already gone, and I have had to pay money out of my own pocket.

Cordially yours,

ALEXANDER BOTTS.

Alexander Botts sings for sales

Super salesman Alexander Botts (Joe E. Brown) gets down on one knee to sing for sales atop a crawler in the 1936 film Earthworm Tractors. *This Earthworm was a thinly disguised Caterpillar RD4. Mabel Johnson (June Travis), the daughter of his toughest sales challenge, looks ready to sign on the dotted line for a tractor.*

EXPENSE ACCOUNT

Railroad fare (Memphis to Cyprus City)	$6.10
Pullman ticket	3.20
Gas and oil for tractor	8.50
Labor (putting on cleats, etc.)	9.00
36 doz. eggs at 50 cents per doz	18.00

(NOTE: It seems the crates we landed on when we dropped off the freight platform were full of eggs.)

1 plate glass window	80.00

(NOTE: I forgot to say in my report that in the confusion following the breaking of the fire plug I accidentally side-swiped a drug store with the tractor.)

Radiator for truck, and labor to install	46.75
Cleaning hat and pressing trousers	3.50
TOTAL	$175.05

(NOTE: I will list the hotel bill, the bill for the fire plug, and other expenses when I pay them.)

FARMERS' FRIEND TRACTOR COMPANY
SALESMAN'S DAILY REPORT
Date: March 21, 1920.
Written from: Delta Hotel, Cyprus City, Miss.
Written by: Alexander Botts.

I will take up the report of my activities at the point where I stopped yesterday when Mr. Johnson had just gotten out of the truck and was coming in my direction. As I stated, he had a great deal to say. Instead of being grateful to me for having given him such a splendid demonstration of the ability of the Earthworm tractor to go through a swamp, and instead of thanking me for saving his life by stopping him just as he was about to shoot over the levee into the Mississippi River, he began using very abusive language which I will not repeat except to say that he told me he would not buy my tractor, and that he never wanted to see me or my damn machinery again. He also said he was going to slam me down in the mud and jump on my face, and it took six of the bystanders to hold him and prevent him from doing this. And although there were six of them, they had a lot of trouble holding him, owing to the fact that he was so wet and slippery from the rain.

As I am a natural born salesman, I saw right away that this was not an auspicious time to give Mr. Johnson any sales talk about tractors. I decided to wait until later, and I walked back to the tractor in a dignified manner, looking back over my shoulder, however, to make sure Mr. Johnson was not getting away from the guys that were holding him.

After they had led Mr. Johnson back to town, I made up my mind to be a good sport, and I hauled his truck into town and left it at the garage to be repaired. The rest of the day I spent settling up various expense items—which appeared on my yesterday's expense account—and in writing up my report. When I finally went to bed at midnight, it was with a glow of pride that I thought of the splendid work I had done on the first day of my employment with the great Farmers' Friend Tractor Company, Makers of Earthworm Tractors. Although I had not as yet made any sales, I could congratulate myself on having put on the best tractor demonstration ever seen in Cyprus City, Mississippi.

This morning, after breakfast, I had a visit from the nice-looking man in the corduroy suit who gave me the buggy ride yesterday.

"I am a lumber operator," he said, "and I have a lot of cyprus back in the swamps that I have been wanting to get out. I haven't been able to move it because the ground has been so soft. However, since I saw your tractor drag that big heavy truck through the swamp yesterday, I know that it is just what I want. I understand the price is $6000, and if you will let me have the machine right away I will take you over to the bank and give you a certified check for that amount."

"Well," I said, "I was supposed to sell this machine to Mr. Johnson, but as he has had a chance at it and hasn't taken it, I suppose I might as well let you have it."

"I don't see why you gave him first chance," said the man in the corduroy suit. "When your other salesman, Mr. Healy, was down here, I gave him more encouragement than anybody else he talked to. And he said he would ship a tractor down here and put on a demonstration for me."

"By the way," I said, "what is your name?"

"William Jackson," he said.

As I have a quick mind, I saw at once what had happened. This was the guy I had been supposed to give the demonstration for in the first place, but I had very naturally confused his name with that of Mr. Johnson. There ought to be a law against two men with such similar names being in the same kind of business in the same town.

However, it had come out all right. And, as I am a natural born salesman, I decided that the thing to do was to take Mr. Jackson over to the bank right away—which I did. And now the tractor is his.

I enclose the certified check. And I have decided to remain in town several days more on the chance of selling some more machines.

Cordially yours,

ALEXANDER BOTTS.

———————

TELEGRAM
EARTHWORM CITY ILLS 1015A MAR 22 1920

ALEXANDER BOTTS
DELTA HOTEL
CYPRUS CITY MISS
YOUR FIRST REPORT AND EXPENSE AC-
COUNT RECEIVED STOP YOU ARE FIRED
STOP WILL DISCUSS THAT EXPENSE AC-
COUNT BY LETTER STOP IF YOU SO MUCH
AS TOUCH THAT TRACTOR AGAIN WE WILL
PROSECUTE YOU TO THE FULLEST EXTENT
OF THE LAW
    FARMERS FRIEND TRACTOR COMPANY
    GILBERT HENDERSON SALES MANAGER

———————

NIGHT LETTER
CYPRUS CITY MISS 510P MAR 22 1920

FARMERS FRIEND TRACTOR CO
EARTHWORM CITY ILLS
YOUR TELEGRAM HERE STOP WAIT TILL
YOU GET MY SECOND REPORT STOP AND
THAT IS NOT ALL STOP THE WHOLE TOWN
IS TALKING ABOUT MY WONDERFUL TRAC-
TOR DEMONSTRATION STOP JOHNSON HAS
COME AROUND AND ORDERED TWO TRAC-
TORS STOP THE LEVEE CONSTRUCTION
COMPANY OF THIS PLACE HAS ORDERED
ONE STOP NEXT WEEK IS TO BE QUOTE USE

MORE TRACTORS WEEK UNQUOTE IN
CYPRUS CITY STOP MASS MEETING
MONDAY TO DECIDE HOW MANY EARTH-
WORMS THE CITY WILL BUY FOR GRADING
ROADS STOP LUMBERMENS MASS MEETING
TUESDAY AT WHICH I WILL URGE THEM TO
BUY TRACTORS AND JACKSON AND
JOHNSON WILL BACK ME UP STOP
WEDNESDAY THURSDAY FRIDAY AND
SATURDAY RESERVED FOR WRITING UP
ORDERS FROM LUMBERMEN CONTRACTORS
AND OTHERS STOP TELL YOUR CHIEF ENGI-
NEER TO GET READY TO INCREASE PRO-
DUCTION STOP YOU BETTER RECONSIDER
YOUR WIRE OF THIS MORNING
                ALEXANDER BOTTS

———————

TELEGRAM
EARTHWORM CITY ILLS 945A MAR 23 1920

ALEXANDER BOTTS
DELTA HOTEL
CYPRUS CITY MISS
OUR WIRE OF YESTERDAY STANDS STOP
YOUR JOB AS SERVICE MECHANIC WITH
THIS COMPANY IS GONE FOREVER STOP WE
ARE PUTTING YOU ON PAY ROLL AS SALES-
MAN STOP TWO HUNDRED PER WEEK PLUS
EXPENSES PLUS FIVE PER CENT COMMIS-
SION ON ALL SALES
    FARMERS FRIEND TRACTOR COMPANY
    GILBERT HENDERSON SALES MANAGER

CHAPTER 6

Building the Nation

The Development of the Construction Equipment Line, 1902–Today

Above: 1960s Caterpillar dealer clock
Owner: Larry Maasdam.

Left: 1934 Caterpillar Diesel Forty and 1938 Elevating Grader Model 42
The elevating grader gouges out a ditch with a disk plow and moves it by a conveyor to a truck bed or to the center of the roadway. Owner: Alan Smith.

The growth in popularity of the automobile spawned a new use for Holt, Best, and the subsequent Caterpillar crawlers—road building. In 1902, the American Automobile Association and the American Road Builders Association were formed. Together, they advocated a national Good Roads Movement. By 1908, individual states were getting on the bandwagon, and legislatures were soon passing funding bills for road construction. State universities held Good Roads Schools, in which construction and maintenance methods were tried and taught.

Benjamin Holt was not one to let an opportunity like this go by. Holt was among the first to recognize the potential of the crawler tractor in road construction, and so his Caterpillar tractors were tested and demonstrated with various dirt-moving and grading implements. Holt's crawlers soon proved themselves superior to wheeled tractors for these purposes.

Graders: Russell and Caterpillar

Pulled graders of many sizes and types were used extensively as early as 1900. These early graders were rated by the number of horses needed to pull them. The crawler tractor soon became the choice for power due to its traction in soft going and its steady slow-speed power. By the end of the 1920s, a Holt 75 trailing as many as three blade graders was a familiar sight.

The Russell Grader Manufacturing Company manufactured most of the graders. The firm was founded in 1903 in Stephen, a small town in the northwest corner of Minnesota, by Richard Russell and his partner, C. K. Stockland. Early production was jobbed out, but in 1906, additional investors came into the company, and it moved to a new factory in Minneapolis.

The first product of the company was an implement known as the elevating grader, invented by Russell and Stockland. The main function of the elevating grader was crowning or contouring a roadbed. In its classic form, the elevating grader gouged out the ditch with a disk plow and, by means of a canvas conveyor, transported the dirt to the center of the road or into a truck driven alongside. Early models were propelled by horses. At first, the rear wheels powered the conveyor; later, an engine was used to improve conveyor operation. At one time, Russell made its own engines for conveyor power, but reverted to ground-wheel power because of cost and reliability considerations. By 1908, Russell was manufacturing graders and scrapers of all types specifically for tractor propulsion.

As early as 1909, Holt was producing a self-propelled road grader featuring a single track on the right and a wheel on the left behind an adjustable blade; a single front wheel provided steering. In an effort to obtain state road money, the unit was called "The Good Roads Machine."

As the forerunner of the modern motor grader, Holt's creation was about a decade before its time.

Holt's idea was sound, however, and Russell soon picked up on it. In 1920, the first Russell self-propelled motor grader was launched as the Motor Patrol No. 1. Power came from an Allis-Chalmers Model 6/12 tractor that was built along the lines of the Universal tractor from the Moline Plow Company of Moline, Illinois—in fact, the Allis 6/12 was so much like the Universal that Moline threatened suit, ending Russell's first attempt at building a motor grader. The Russell Motor Patrol No. 2 followed in 1925 with Fordson propulsion; the Motor Patrol No. 3 used a McCormick-Deering 10/20.

In 1925, Russell married a Holt 2-Ton to one of its graders to produce its successful Motor Patrol No. 4. After the merger of Holt and Best, this motor grader caught

Horse-powered road grader, 1912
In the days before crawlers took over, roads were graded by horse-drawn graders, such as this setup pulled by eight horses in Kansas. (Smithsonian Institution)

1925 Russell No. 2 motor grader
Russell's long-wheelbase No. 2 was powered by a Fordson engine and featured tight-fitting controls. This motor grader rode on the Trackson crawler conversion. The No. 2 was also available with hard rubber drive wheels.

Russell grader, 1990s
Author Robert Pripps maintains the mile of dirt road to his maple syrup operation in Northern Wisconsin with his medium-size Russell Standard grader and styled John Deere Model B tractor.

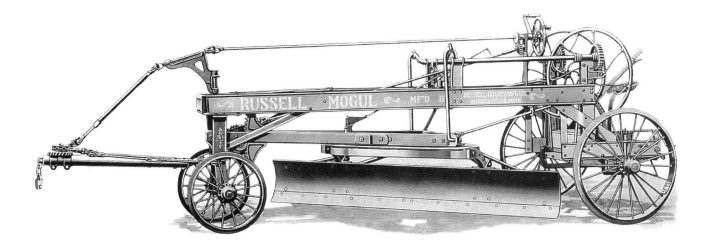

1910s Russell Mogul grader
Sized for the Best Sixty or Holt 10-Ton tractors, Russell offered its Mogul grader between 1913 and 1922. It was replaced by the refined Super Mogul. Both weighed 10,000 pounds (4,500 kg).

1920s Caterpillar No. 2 grader
Caterpillar's grader line was acquired when Cat purchased Russell in 1928. Owner: Alan Smith.

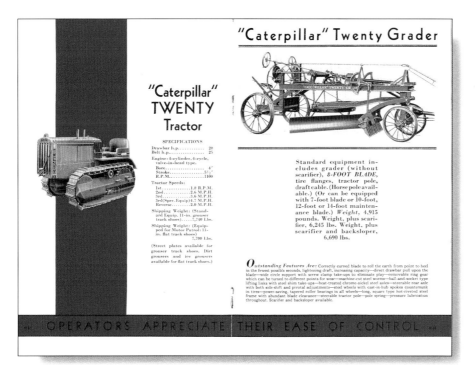

1920s Caterpillar Twenty tractor and grader
After Caterpillar purchased the Russell firm, Cat crawlers and graders were designed to work together.

1930s Caterpillar Russell brochure

the attention of Caterpillar, which arranged to purchase the Russell outfit in 1928.

Russell had offered its Motor Patrol No. 5 in 1927 with Cletrac power, but when Caterpillar acquired Russell in 1928, the No. 5 was replaced with the No. 6, based on the Cat Twenty.

Caterpillar modernized the entire line of pull graders in 1929 and added new sizes to the motor grader line with model numbers changed to reflect Caterpillar nomenclature. The Motor Patrol No. 10, for example, used a Cat Ten power unit, and the Caterpillar Sixty pull grader was for use with the Sixty tractor.

Control of the blade and wheel angles was motorized on both pull and motor graders from the beginning of

the 1930s. Power was applied through a series of hand-controlled clutches: Pull types used small engines to drive the clutch box in front of the operator, while Motor Patrols received control power from the drive engine.

A new Auto Patrol line of motor graders came out in 1931, while the Great Depression raged and most of Cat's research resources were devoted to its revolutionary diesel engine. The Auto Patrol was not based on an existing tractor, but was designed from the ground up to be a road grader. This was the first grader to mount the engine in the rear to improve operator visibility and traction. Auto Patrols No. 7 and No. 9 made their debut in 1932, followed by the No. 10 in 1933 and No. 11 in 1934. A diesel engine option was also offered in 1934. By 1936, the No.

1934 Caterpillar Diesel Forty and 1938 Elevating Grader Model 42
This Model 42 Elevating Grader, serial number 1G188, was powered by a D4 engine to operate the conveyor.

1934 Caterpillar Diesel Forty and 1938 Elevating Grader Model 42
Aboard his Diesel Forty, owner Alan Smith pulls his restored Caterpillar Elevating Grader.

10 and No. 11, which shared a common frame, were offered with tandem drive axles and the graders were close to their final form. The No. 10 later evolved into the No. 112 grader.

When the No. 11 Auto Patrol arrived in 1936, it was Caterpillar's largest motor grader. It used the 4.50x5.50-inch (112.50x137.50-mm) engine from the Caterpillar Twenty-Five tractor, although the cylinders were cast in pairs and a different manifold was used. Equipment included an oil-pressure gauge, starter, generator, lights, horn, rear-wheel brakes, and a transmission brake.

Destined to become Caterpillar's longest-produced motor grader, the No. 12 was introduced in 1938 using the D6 engine, although the R6 gas engine was optional. In 1965, the clutch-type power controls were replaced with hydraulic-driven mechanical controls on the Model No. 12F. Finally, direct hydraulic controls were fitted to No. 12G, introduced in 1973. The No. 12 was still in the inventory in 1999 as the No. 12H. Sixty years and counting— not a bad record for a machine design.

When the No. 12 came out, Caterpillar also introduced a number of other graders that were similar to the No. 12, but smaller in size. They included the D4-powered No. 112 and the D2-powered No. 212.

The largest Caterpillar grader in 1999 was the 131,000-pound (58,950-kg) Model 24H. It was designed specifically for maintaining mine roads where heavy-hauler trucks operated.

Scrapers:
LeTourneau and Caterpillar

The first known tractor-powered scraper was invented by Henry Lage, who built his Ground Plane in about 1912. The machine consisted of a large slip (also known as a Fresno) scraper pan with wheels. Through a system of belts, power from the wheels was applied to load and dump the pan. The invention must have been an impressive improvement: In 1914, Holt bought the rights to the machine, and the Ground Plane became the Caterpillar Land Leveler.

In 1915, excavation contractor Theodore Schmeiser received a patent for his own Land Leveler, an invention that revolutionized earthmoving. Built by the Schmeiser Manufacturing Company of Davis (and later Fresno), California, the machine had two 78-inch (195-cm) wheels that carried the rear of a graderlike arch; the front of the arch was connected to a tractor drawbar. Suspended under the arch like a grader blade was a scoop resembling a large slip scraper. The operator rode on the rear platform and lowered the front of the scoop. As the tractor and Land Leveler proceeded forward, the scoop scraped up dirt. With the aid of compressed air, the operator raised and lowered the front of the scoop according to the limit of the tractor until the scoop was full. The front of the scoop was then raised to its maximum height—which was only a few inches above ground—to prevent the dirt from spilling while the load was transported. The rear of the

1952 Caterpillar No. 212 motor grader
The No. 212 grader was powered by Cat's 50-hp D311 diesel engine, which was also used in the D2 crawler. As equipped with a 12-foot (360-cm) blade, scarifier, and leaning oversized front wheels, it weighed 15,000 pounds (6,750 kg). The cab was equipped with windshield wipers, defroster fan, and heater. Owner: Kent Bates.

1952 Caterpillar No. 212 motor grader
The blade mechanism of the No. 212 motor grader was powered by the grader's engine through driver-controlled clutches. Hydraulic grader controls did not arrive until the mid-1960s.

Caterpillar Diesel pulling LeTourneau scraper, 1931
Robert LeTourneau developed his Land Leveler scraper so it could be controlled by electric motors operated from his Holt 75 tractor. His scrapers became the industry standard.

scoop dragged on the ground. After the fashion of the slip scraper, the scoop was dumped by air pressure.

The tractor drawing the Land Leveler had to be modified to drive an air compressor to keep the storage receiver on the Land Leveler filled; Schmeiser had a cooperative arrangement with the C. L. Best Gas Tractor Company to fit tractors with the compressors.

The Schmeiser Land Leveler inspired another Stockton, California, inventor named Robert Gilmore LeTourneau. LeTourneau loved to move earth. Born in 1888, he built his first earthmoving machine at age 12 according to his autobiography, *Mover of Men and Mountains*, published in 1960. LeTourneau was not satisfied with the operation of his Schmeiser Land Leveler, so he modified it to be controlled by electric motors. Now he could control each side separately from his Holt 75 tractor. Never one to be content, LeTourneau continued making improvements to the scraper-transporter concept, working closely with Holt and Best, and later with Caterpillar. In the early 1930s, LeTourneau and his equipment teamed with famed industrialist Henry J. Kaiser to construct the Hoover Dam.

In 1934, LeTourneau followed Caterpillar to the Midwest, also setting up his manufacturing facility in Peoria. By then he was also making bulldozer blades, cable power units, and other tractor-powered implements. Caterpillar would load a crawler on a flatcar in East Peoria and send it over to LeTourneau's factory to have a blade installed or a scraper attached. Then the flatcar would be directed to the final customer. Caterpillar dealers also sold LeTourneau scrapers. LeTourneau earthmovers and Caterpillar tractors built many of the early roads of North America, bringing prosperity to both companies and to Peoria.

All worked well until the late 1930s, when LeTourneau announced its new Turnapull, a combination rubber-tired, two-wheeled tractor with a permanently attached scraper that once again revolutionized earthmoving. With its rubber tires, the rig was much faster on the haul, and what it lacked in straight pulling power could be made up for by a crawler tractor pushing it through the loading process. There was some sales resistance at first, since the tractor part was dependent on the scraper for support, but the Turnapull ultimately proved itself.

1934 Caterpillar Diesel Seventy-Five and LeTourneau scraper

The Seventy-Five was a big tractor, weighing in at 32,000 pounds (14,400 kg), making it ideal for operating a LeTourneau scraper with ease. The Diesel Seventy-Five used the same starting motor as the Diesel Sixty-Five and Diesel Seventy. There were gas versions of the Sixty-Five and Seventy, but only the diesel version of the Seventy-Five. Owner: Larry Simon.

1934 Caterpillar Diesel Seventy-Five and LeTourneau scraper

The Diesel Seventy-Five was made from 1933 to 1935 and boasted 93 hp from its 5.25x8.00-inch (131.25x200-mm), six-cylinder engine. Made from 1933 to 1935, the Diesel Seventy-Five was an outgrowth of the Diesel Seventy, which was made only in 1933. With more minor changes it became the RD8.

Above: 1940s Caterpillar DW10

Caterpillar's first rubber-tired tractor, the DW10, was introduced in 1940 and designed to pull scrapers at higher speeds than crawlers could muster. A crawler was required to push the DW10 and scraper through the loading cycle, however. Author Robert Pripps is at the controls. Owner: Neil Koshak.

Left: 1940s Caterpillar DW10

The DW10 was powered by a D6 engine of 90 hp, which made it the most powerful rubber tired tractor of its day. It used a five-speed transmission. This DW10 still earns its keep at Koshak Construction Company in Park Falls, Wisconsin, where it pulls a wobble-wheel roller. Owner Neil Koshak got the tractor from the U.S. Army Corps of Engineers in the mid-1970s, and also has the cab that came with it.

Above: 1940s Trackson T4 Traxcavator loader
Trackson's T4 was based on the Caterpillar D4, and bears se-rial number 5T6838W. Owner: Dan Plote.

Right: 1940s Trackson T4 Traxcavator loader
The T4 Traxcavator loader was cable operated. In 1951, Cat-erpillar bought the rights to Trackson patents and incorpo-rated them into in-house designs.

LeTourneau's move to providing motive power for his scrapers caused a rift in the otherwise good relations be-tween LeTourneau and Caterpillar. Caterpillar countered with its first rubber-tired tractor, the DW-10, and Cater-pillar-brand towed scrapers and dump wagons. A 90-hp D6 engine powered the DW-10. It was a conventional four-wheel rig that could be mated to scrapers from other manufacturers, or adapted to a variety of different uses.

Starting in 1951, Caterpillar developed a complete line of earthmoving equipment, including two-wheel tractor-scraper combos. By 1999, Caterpillar's largest rubber-tired scraper, the 657E, was a two-engined job with a combined flywheel power rating of 950 hp. This item could move 44 yards (40 meters) of dirt at some 20 mph (32 kph).

Loaders: Trackson and Caterpillar

The Trackson Company was founded in Milwaukee, Wisconsin, in 1922, to offer a full tracked conversion for Henry Ford's ubiquitous Fordson wheeled tractor. The Fordson was a lightweight and inexpensive farm tractor designed to do for the farmer what the Model T had done for the pedestrian. Because it was light yet fairly powerful, the Fordson had notoriously poor traction. The Trackson outfit corrected that deficiency with its crawler conversion. But when Ford transferred Fordson production to Ireland in 1927, Trackson was left out in the cold. By 1928, it had an arrangement to design and build a tractor chassis for the Allis-Chalmers Company of Milwaukee. But then Allis-Chalmers acquired the crawler line of the Monarch Tractor Company of Watertown, Wisconsin, and the deal was off.

With encouragement from Caterpillar, Trackson entered the accessory business, developing a line of pipe layers, augers, bulldozer blades, and finally, its Traxcavator, a cable-operated front-end loader. While some of these items were sold to others, most went to Caterpillar. In 1951, Caterpillar bought the Trackson Company patents and incorporated them into its designs.

While the Traxcavator was the first volume-production front-end loader, the invention of the basic machine dated back to 1926 and the Killefer Manufacturing Company of Fresno, California, which was later acquired by Deere & Company of Moline, Illinois. The Killefer loader was simply a cable-operated bucket, or pan, attached to the front of a Holt 5-Ton. A similar device was made by the now-famous Hough Company of Berkeley, California.

The industry's first tracked front-end loader designed from the ground up was the Caterpillar No. 6, introduced in 1952. In 1959, the first Caterpillar wheel-type loader, the Model 944 was unveiled. This was followed in 1963 by the first Caterpillar articulated wheel loaders, the Models 966 and 988.

Engines

Holt, the two Best firms, and Caterpillar have probably made more different engine types and sizes than any other tractor company. In fact, they have probably made a larger variety of engines than any of the automobile companies.

As early as 1889, Daniel Best's company produced its first steam engine. Holt followed suit in 1890, and a variety of steamers were produced over the next two decades. In 1908, spark-ignition engines began to replace steam in Holt and Best tractors. Again, a large variety of kerosene and gasoline-fueled engines emerged from their factories—especially from Holt, which had its own separate engine company, Aurora.

1940s Trackson T4 Traxcavator loader
The Trackson Company was founded in Milwaukee, Wisconsin, to manufacture a crawler conversion kit for Henry Ford's lightweight Fordson farm tractor. When Fordson production was transferred to Ireland, Trackson developed other equipment, such as this Traxcavator loader.

Caterpillar grader engine
This 5-hp, single-cylinder Caterpillar engine provided onboard power to pull grader serial number 5E99. The engine, which weighed 540 pounds (243 kg), powered the grader blade.

1960s Caterpillar D6B
Also known as the DW6, the D6B rubber-tired tractors were especially useful in sugar cane fields. The design originated with the Clewiston Motor Company of Clewiston, Florida.

When C. L. Best and Holt formed Caterpillar in 1925, work began in earnest on a diesel tractor engine. Spending more than $1 million over the next six years—the equivalent of $100 million today—Caterpillar created the world's first commercial mobile diesel engine, the D9900, which powered the diesel version of the Sixty crawler.

The D17000 V-8 diesel was the first Caterpillar diesel specifically designed for marine propulsion, although it was also sold for industrial purposes. By 1935, five sizes of diesels were made, ranging in power from 47 to 130 hp.

In 1939, Caterpillar introduced a diesel generator set, the first engine-generator set from a single manufacturer. The first Caterpillar diesel specifically designed for truck use also arrived in 1939 in the form of the six-cylinder D468 rated at 90 hp at 1,800 rpm. A four-cylinder version, the 60-hp D312, was also offered.

Among other interesting uses for Caterpillar diesel engines, a D13000 engine was installed in the freighter *Muriel Eileen* in 1940. The 65-foot-long (19.5-meter) vessel features 300 hp turning a 42-inch (105-cm) propeller making the ship capable of 8.75 knots. Originally built in 1926 as a freighter, the *Muriel Eileen* later in life served as a crab dredge and as an oyster transporter. She is now owned and being restored by David M. Cantera of New Castle, Delaware.

At the same time the diesel was being created, gas engine development continued for the smaller Caterpillar tractors. A series of small one-cylinder gas engines were made to power the controls of Caterpillar pull-type road graders. Most of the Cat diesels had gas starting motors, so a variety of engines were produced for this purpose. Three-, four-, and six-cylinder gas engines were made for motor graders.

In 1931, a department within Caterpillar Marketing was formed to handle engine sales to outside customers. The first D9900 sold outside of Caterpillar went to the Thew Shovel Company of Lorain, Ohio, in June 1932; Thew built a 1½-yard (1.2-cubic-meter) power shovel propelled by the Cat engine. By 1938, more than a hundred outside companies were buying Cat diesels for diverse applications including irrigation pumping, electric power generating, power shovels, and cotton gins. Other manufacturers were by then also building mobile diesels, but Caterpillar enjoyed one-third of the world market.

Solar Turbines, a wholly owned subsidiary of Caterpillar, produces a variety of large gas turbine engines. Rated from 1,590 to 18,000 hp, these clean-burning engines are used in applications such as electric power generation, pipe line pumping, oil and gas production, and ship propulsion. Solar Turbines is headquartered in San Diego, California.

Caterpillar Collector Profile: Kent C. Bates

One of the more interesting young Cat collectors is Kent Bates of Chillicothe, Illinois. He is a hands-on collector-restorer with his own machine shop. Bates was born in a farming community in Kansas and graduated from Kansas State University. He tells this story about his grandfather: "Granddad farmed with mules until 1938, at which time he bought a Caterpillar Twenty-Two. He continued farming with crawlers, upgrading to a D2 in the mid-1940s. He was the only farmer in the community to use crawlers and in fact never owned a rubber-tired tractor."

Bates moved to Illinois in the early 1970s and brought with him some original Caterpillar service tools inherited from his grandfather. The Bates spread is on the end of a dirt road in the country. One of its interesting features is a 1926 Gordon–Van Tyne kit barn. In those days, several companies, including Sears Roebuck, sold kit buildings by mail, including kits for homes. The Gordon–Van Tyne kit included everything but gravel and water for the cement. Step-by-step directions were provided, as were nails, shingles, windows, and paint. The barn is now filled with Caterpillar tractors and spare parts.

Bates is active in the Antique Caterpillar Machinery Owner's Club and is a member of the national board of directors. Along with other members, Bates has developed authentic decal kits for vintage Caterpillar tractors, created the club's website, and is assembling a complete serial number yearbook for all antique Caterpillar machinery and accessories—a monumental project.

Caterpillar 30 KW generator set
This D4600 Power unit used a D6 diesel engine of 4.25x5.50 inches (106.25x137.50 mm). It had a 30 KW Louis Allis self-regulating generator. Owner: Ray Zander. (Photograph © Robert N. Pripps)

1943 Caterpillar D4 with LeTourneau blade
This early J Series D4 was fitted with a LeTourneau blade and Hyster winch. Owner: Larry Simon.

1943 Caterpillar D4 with LeTourneau blade
It served with the U.S. Coast Guard in Michigan's Upper Peninsula, where it was used for pulling boats out of the water and repairing sea walls. The Coast Guard overhauled it in 1971.

CHAPTER 7

Modern Caterpillar

The Ongoing History of Caterpillar, 1946–Today

Above: 1981 Caterpillar D9L brochure

Left: 1993 Caterpillar Challenger 85D
For the serious farmer, the Challenger 85D offers the pull and traction needed for big tillage jobs. The 85 weighs in at more than 20 tons (18,000 kg). Owner: Duane Janikula.

Following World War I, huge amounts of military construction equipment were returned to the United States and sold as surplus. This played a part in devastating the postwar market and helped spark an economic recession. Following World War II, these lessons were not forgotten by President Harry S. Truman's administration. Thousands of pieces of heavy equipment were left on the Pacific Islands or dumped overboard from ships. While it was seen by some as an appalling waste, companies like Caterpillar were able to convert to peacetime production and commercial selling with a minimum of disruption.

Backlog orders in 1946 were the largest in Caterpillar history. In the next seven years, 3 million square feet (270,000 square meters) of factory space were added, and the production of new models was underway. Two new test and proving ground facilities were opened in Arizona and Peoria. A new plant was also opened in Joliet, Illinois.

New products were developed in the decade after the war. The DW20 and DW21 wheeled tractors were rolled out with Caterpillar scrapers, and four new diesel engines were unveiled. The Trackson Company in Milwaukee was acquired and all-new Caterpillar track-loaders were developed.

In 1950, Caterpillar took its first step toward multinationalism when the first overseas subsidiary was established, Caterpillar Tractor Company, Ltd., of Coalville, Leicestershire, Great Britain. This enterprise was to manufacture, store, and distribute parts to British dealers, who could be paid in British pounds. Thus, problems of customs, taxes, and exchange rates were eliminated. Manufacturing facilities in France, Belgium, Mexico, Australia, Brazil, and South Africa followed. New products and updated versions of existing products were being shipped to more than 800 dealer outlets worldwide.

Tractors

Caterpillar's D2, D4, D6, D7, and D8 diesel crawlers produced in 1946 and 1947 were virtually the same as the prewar and wartime tractors, but none of the gas tractors survived for postwar production.

The classic U Series came out in 1947. The D2 engine bore was enlarged from 3.75 to 4.00 inches (93.75 to 100 mm), upping power to 32 drawbar hp. It weighed in at a little over 7,000 pounds.

The D4 engine also got the 0.25-inch (6.25-mm) bore increase of the D2, making the bore and stroke 4.50x5.50 inches (112.50x137.50 mm). This four-cylinder engine used a new cross-flow cylinder head. The U Series D6 used the same engine design, but had six cylinders. The D4 weighed 11,000 pounds (4,950 kg), while the D6 weighed 19,000 pounds (8,550 kg).

The D5 (9M) tractor was both introduced and discontinued in 1939. The D5 had the same running gear as the D4 (7J) with the optional five-roller track. The engine was the six-cylinder version of the standard 4.50x5.50-inch (112.50x137.50-mm) powerplant and rated at 45 drawbar hp; this Model D-4600 engine was later used in the 1941–1947 six-cylinder D6. Some forty-six D5s were built for a special government order. The D5 was resurrected in 1966 and is still in production today.

D7s and D8s shared a standard 5.75x8.00-inch (143.75x200-mm) engine, four cylinders in the D7 and six in the D8. Engine and injection system improvements steadily raised power over the following years: The D8 was up to 155 hp by the end of the U Series in 1955 while the D8F-14A of 1955 offered 191 flywheel hp. The D7 weighed 30,000 pounds (13,500 kg) and the D8 37,000 pounds (16,650 kg). All of the U Series Caterpillar crawlers used five-speed transmissions. The D8H of 1958 offered a three-speed power shift and torque converter transmission.

1954 Caterpillar advertisement
This ad celebrated "50 Years on Tracks." Besides the D8, an early Holt steam crawler was pictured.

1947 Caterpillar D4 Orchard
The D4 U Series featured a new 4.50x5.50-inch (112.50x137.50-mm) engine with cross-flow cylinder heads. The 350-ci (5,733-cc) diesel engine produced 421 foot-pounds of torque at 1,000 rpm. It normally used a two-cylinder, horizontally opposed starting motor with a 2.75x3.00-inch (68.75x75-mm) bore and stroke, but this example has direct electric start. Author Robert Pripps is at the controls. Owner: Larry Maasdam.

Above: **Bird's-eye view of the Caterpillar factory in Peoria, Illinois, 1930s**

Right: **Caterpillar factory in Peoria, Illinois, 1940s**

With its new D9 in 1954, Caterpillar stood alone at the peak of the horsepower heap—until the giant D9 was topped by other Cats. The D9's new turbo six-cylinder engine measured 6.25x8.00 inches(156.25x200 mm) and displaced 1,473 ci (24,128 cc). It developed more than half again as much power as the D8. The D9 weighed more than 66,000 pounds (29,700 kg). A unique feature of the D9 was its hydraulically boosted clutch controls, which made this monster much easier to drive.

By 1970, competitors were catching up in the power race. Caterpillar announced an interesting variation on the D9—the Quad-Track D9G, featuring two D9s connected one behind the other with the operator riding in the front compartment. The 1974 version weighed 180,000 pounds (81,000 kg) and generated 820 flywheel hp. A second double-header was the SxS D9G with two D9s side by side, pushing one 24-foot-wide (7.2-meter) dozer blade. Again, 820 flywheel hp was available, but weight was 186,000 pounds (83,700 kg).

In 1966, the Special Application (SA) D4, D5, and D6 tractors were introduced especially for agriculture. These designs had the engines shifted forward for better balance while doing drawbar work. Another feature added to the SA tractors was Variable Horsepower: When third, fourth, or fifth gear was selected, an electric switch moved the injector rack stop, allowing the engine to produce 35 percent more hp. This feature allowed much faster agricultural work, without having to beef up the drivetrain to take the additional torque produced through first and second gears. The D7 SA was added to the Special Application Series in 1977, followed by the D8 SA in 1984. This series of agricultural tractors had greatly increased productivity in the 2.5 to 5 mph (4–8 kph) range most often desired for fieldwork.

A sealed and lubricated track system was the next big feature. Coming into production in 1976, this feature greatly reduced wear on the components that have always been a major part of the cost of crawler operation. Next, Caterpillar borrowed a page from its own Best Humpback of 1913, introducing elevated-sprocket crawler tracks. These elevated drive sprockets were first used on the Humpback and later copied by the 1920 Cletrac Model F. Caterpillar determined that elevated sprockets isolated

Left, top: 1947 Caterpillar D4 Orchard
Note the sparse instrumentation, par for the late 1940s.

Left, bottom: 1947 Caterpillar D4 Orchard
Control of devices by external hydraulic cylinder was just becoming accepted practice in the late 1940s, and this D4 had an added hydraulic pump and tank. The pump was driven directly from the engine crankshaft.

Above: 1947 Caterpillar D4 Orchard
Maximum power was 59 hp at 1,600 rpm. The U Series D4 used a five-speed gearbox.

Left: 1947 Caterpillar D4 Orchard
Caterpillar orchard tractors use this type of a low, or "tail," seat. It kept the operator low for passing under the tree branches, and also allowed for control of towed implements.

Below: 1940s Caterpillar dealer clock
Owner: Larry Maasdam.

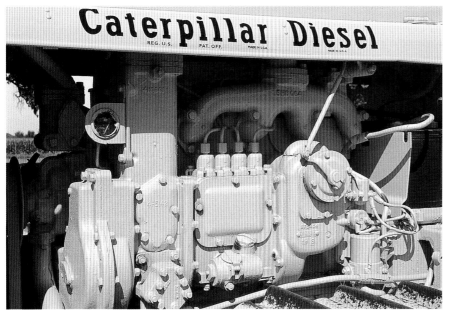

Above: 1950s Caterpillar D2 Orchard
A two-cylinder starting motor was used, although 24-volt direct electric starting was an option, as fitted to this D2.

Facing page, top: 1950s Caterpillar D2 Orchard
During University of Nebraska testing, the D2 demonstrated a maximum pull of almost 7,500 pounds (3,375 kg), or 88 percent of its own weight of 8,500 pounds (3,825 kg). This D2 Orchard is serial number 5U18696. Owner: Larry Maasdam.

Facing page, center: 1950s Caterpillar D2 Orchard
The Caterpillar D2 used a four-cylinder diesel engine of 252 ci (4,128 cc). Maximum power was 42 hp at 1,150 rpm.

Facing page, bottom: 1950s Caterpillar D2 Orchard
The orchard version of the D2 had a low tail seat. Note the bend in the steering levers: Only the latest of the U Series tractors had these; earlier tractors had straight levers.

Top: 1953 Caterpillar D6
Owner Larry Maasdam looks to be at home on this D6 "Hard Nose." He should, as he's owned it since he was eighteen years old. This is the machine he started his construction business with. It has a Caterpillar hydraulic blade.

Above: 1950s Caterpillar D6-9U
This D6-9U featured special wide treads for flotation. Owner Alan Smith still uses it for powering a large pump.

Right: 1950s Caterpillar D6-9U
Hydraulics added to the front of the D6-9U were an option in the 1940s and 1950s.

Above: 1950s Caterpillar D6-9U
The D6-9U weighs just under 10 tons (9,000 kg), but the special wide treads allow it to travel over owner Alan Smith's lawn leaving hardly a mark.

Left: 1950s Caterpillar D6-9U
This D6-9U was fitted with a 24-volt direct electric starter.

clutches and brakes from shock and protected the highly loaded sprockets from much of the dirt, water, and debris that are normal for crawler operations.

The new D10 came out in 1976 sporting elevated-sprocket technology. The D10 had a remarkable, ultra-modern V-12 engine with dual turbochargers and four valves per cylinder. The 1,786-ci (29,255-cc) engine had a rated operating speed of 1,800 rpm and produced 700 flywheel hp. The D9L came out in 1980, also with elevated sprocket and a V-12 engine. The D9L was replaced in 1987 by the D10N, which was replaced by the D10R in 1996. The D10 was upgraded into the new model D11N in 1986, the D11R in 1996, and the D11R CD Carrydozer, also in 1996. Power from the big V-8 engine was 850 hp in 1999.

Loaders

After the purchase of Trackson by Caterpillar in 1951, all-Caterpillar cable-operated loaders based on the D2, D4, D6, and D7 were produced. A hydraulically operated HT4 was also available, based on the D4. The Model No. 6 Traxcavator was introduced in 1952. It was the first modern, all-hydraulic track-loader and the forerunner of a long line of front- and rear-engined loaders.

Large, rubber-tired loaders were pioneered by the Hough Company and the Michigan firm of Detroit, Michigan. Caterpillar joined the market in 1959, and was soon excavating its share of sales. The Model No. 944A could be obtained with a 105-hp diesel or gas engine. The 944A was not articulated, but was steered by its rear wheels.

1958 Caterpillar 955

The 955's engine was basically a D4 unit, but had a balancer that allowed an operating speed of 2,050 rpm. It had a two-cylinder pony motor, although direct electric start was an option. The undercarriage was basically the same as that of the D6.

1960s Caterpillar D8H

The D8H was built between 1958 and 1974. This machine waits for work at Bud Henderson's sales lot in Aledo, Illinois.

1960s Caterpillar D6B

The D6B was made in Peoria from 1959 to 1963, and built overseas as late as 1968. This D6B was ready for a new assignment at Bud Henderson's in Aledo, Illinois.

Facing page: 1958 Caterpillar 955

Owner Alan Smith bought this 955 (12A Series E) machine in 1958 when he was just twenty years old and the crawler had worked only 900 hours. With this machine, he started Alan Smith Excavating, and the 955 now has more than 20,000 hours on the clock.

1960 Caterpillar dealer clock
Owner: Larry Maasdam.

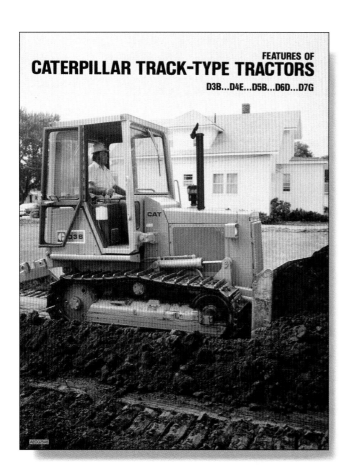

1970s Caterpillar brochure
This brochure advertised the latest D3B, D4E, D5B, D6D, and D7G.

Larger and smaller versions followed. Articulated wheel loaders arrived in 1963 with the Models 988 and 966B. These were originally called Traxcavators, as were the track loaders, but the name was dropped in 1965 because of customer confusion.

Backhoe-loaders based on wheeled farm tractors were pioneered in 1956 by J. I. Case of Racine, Wisconsin. This machine proved so handy and useful that similar machines from Deere, Ford, and John Charles Bamford's JCB Landpower Ltd. of Cheadle, Staffordshire, England, were soon on the market. Add-on units became available at around the same time, by manufacturers such as the Sherman Bros. Implement Company of Evansville, Indiana. Caterpillar joined the fray in 1985 with its Model 416 and soon established itself as a strong competitor. The line grew to include the most modern loader-backhoes. As an example, the 1996 436C offered an 85-hp turbo-diesel engine and all-wheel steering.

Haulers

Caterpillar began working with rubber-tired tractors on its DW10 of 1939. After World War II, an upgraded DW20 tractor was introduced with 345 hp. The DW21 was a two-wheel tractor introduced in 1951 with a 275-hp engine. These were coupled to Caterpillar scrapers. Today, rubber-tired tractor scrapers boast more than 500 hp and can attain loaded speeds of more than 30 mph (48 kph). When it comes to loading and transporting material over longer distances, it is hard to beat these haulers.

1950s Caterpillar D9
This D9 still has the famous FABCO dealer sticker on it. The D9 was introduced in 1954, with full production as the D9D beginning in 1955. The current designation is D9R. Koshak Construction Company owns this one.

The first of the off-road dump trucks from Caterpillar, the pug-nosed Model 769, was unveiled in 1962. This was a 375-hp, 35-ton (31,500-kg), rear-dump machine. It was followed by ever-larger mechanical-drive units, culminating in the 23-foot-tall (6.9-meter) Model 797, due for production in 2001 with a capacity of 360 tons (324,000 kg).

Other off-road truck makers of the 1960s were delivering diesel-electric trucks with drivetrains fashioned after conventional railroad engines. In 1964, Caterpillar experimented with its Models 779 and 783, both powered by 1,000-hp V-12 diesels. The Model 786 used two of the 1,000-hp engines. After 1967, a few of the 779 versions were delivered to customers, but Caterpillar engineers began to see that mechanical drive would offer more advantages. Therefore, the electric-drive trucks were bought back from their owners in 1969 and scrapped.

Following in the heritage of the DW10 and DW20 were the new articulated haulers. These were actually four-wheel rubber-tired tractors with large bottom-dump two-wheel goose-neck trailers. Many of these rigs used trailers made by others for specific duties, but in 1975, the Model 776 Coal Hauler was unveiled. It was a complete Caterpillar outfit, including the 870-hp tractor and the 150-ton (135,000-kg) bottom-dump trailer. Total loaded weight was 500,000 pounds (225,000 kg).

Road Machinery

Caterpillar provided ten sizes of road graders by the 1990s, including the venerable Model 12. Power ranged from 125 to 500 hp and weights from 28,000 to 131,000 pounds (12,600–58,950 kg). In addition, there were compactors, cold planers, pavers, and soil stabilizers. Integrated tool carriers handled a variety of road jobs with a range of attachments. Excavators and shovels rounded out the line of construction equipment, although such items were also used for mining and other earthmoving chores.

Engines

Caterpillar manufactured a variety of prime movers for stationary and mobile industrial applications, marine vessels, locomotives, generator sets, and trucks. Cat formally entered the diesel engine sales field in 1968, although it had been selling tractor engines to other original equipment manufacturers (OEMs) for more than thirty years. The first engine series was the Cat 3400, and a new factory in Mossville, Illinois, was built to produce this and subsequent series. The 1980s saw the 3200, 3300, 3400, 3500, and 3600 Series engines on the market. Each series had a common displacement per cylinder, but could be obtained with from four to sixteen cylinders.

1980 Caterpillar D10 brochure

For the 1990s, the 3114, 3116, 3126, and 3176 Series engines were added. These were inline engines with the last digit indicating the number of cylinders. The middle two digits indicated the displacement per cylinder in liters. In 1998, some more new engines were added with a new designation system. On the C7 and C9, for example, the numbers denoted engine displacement in liters.

Forestry

One of the first jobs assigned to Holt and Best steam tractors was the hauling of logs out of the woods. All sizes of Caterpillar crawlers, except for the largest, have participated in the logging process. In 1985, however, Caterpillar went into the business in a new way, building specialized forestry skidders. These were followed by log loaders, feller bunchers, and harvesters.

As of 1999, Caterpillar was the only manufacturer to build a track-type grapple skidder. This machine was capable of grabbing a clutch of logs near their ends, picking them up full length, and carrying them to the landing. The tracks allowed operation in soft, wet, and steep terrain with a minimum of damage to the forest floor.

Above: Modern Caterpillar D11N

The D11N is king of the hill in any language. A 770-hp, V-8 Model 3508 engine provides 10 percent more push than the D10N due to its aftercooling and turbocharging. (Caterpillar, Inc.)

Right: Modern Caterpillar D9N boarding ship

On its way to Russia, this D9 was ordered without the roll-over protection structure (ROPS), cab, and dozer blade. Foreign sales are an even more important part of marketing today than in the 1930s. (Caterpillar, Inc.)

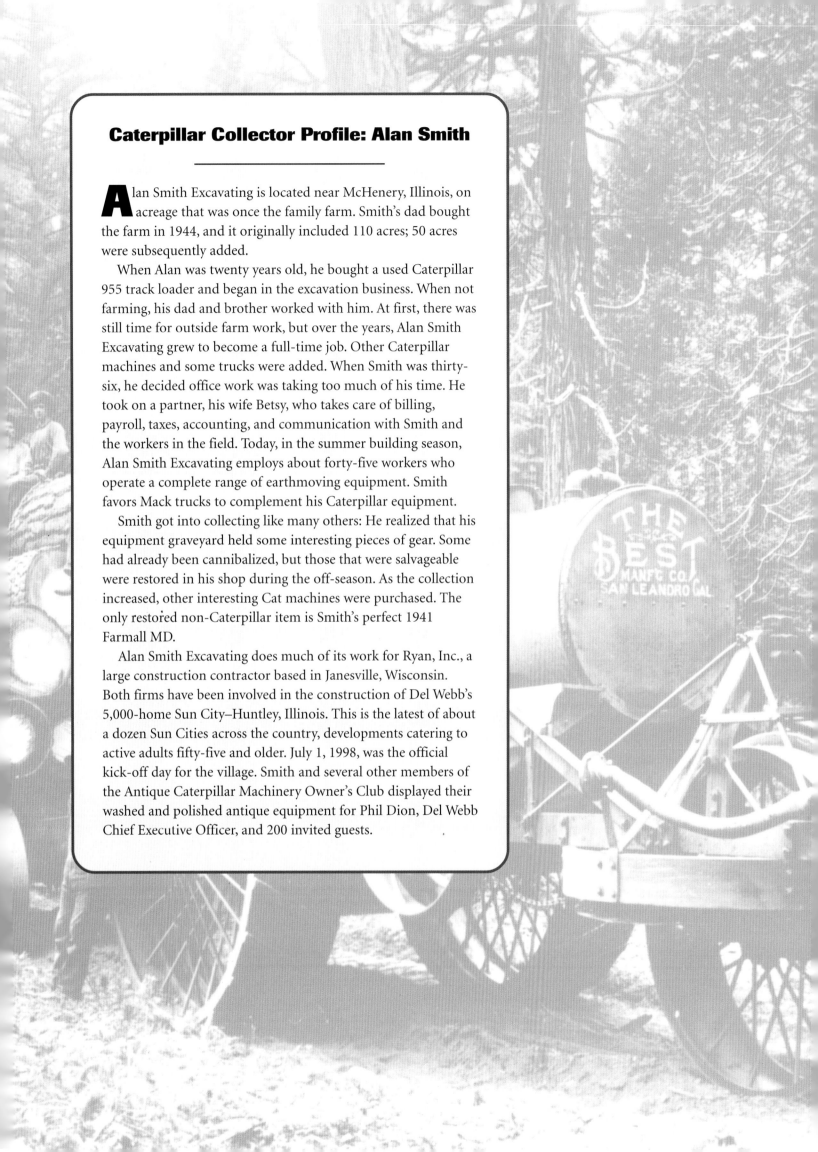

Caterpillar Collector Profile: Alan Smith

Alan Smith Excavating is located near McHenery, Illinois, on acreage that was once the family farm. Smith's dad bought the farm in 1944, and it originally included 110 acres; 50 acres were subsequently added.

When Alan was twenty years old, he bought a used Caterpillar 955 track loader and began in the excavation business. When not farming, his dad and brother worked with him. At first, there was still time for outside farm work, but over the years, Alan Smith Excavating grew to become a full-time job. Other Caterpillar machines and some trucks were added. When Smith was thirty-six, he decided office work was taking too much of his time. He took on a partner, his wife Betsy, who takes care of billing, payroll, taxes, accounting, and communication with Smith and the workers in the field. Today, in the summer building season, Alan Smith Excavating employs about forty-five workers who operate a complete range of earthmoving equipment. Smith favors Mack trucks to complement his Caterpillar equipment.

Smith got into collecting like many others: He realized that his equipment graveyard held some interesting pieces of gear. Some had already been cannibalized, but those that were salvageable were restored in his shop during the off-season. As the collection increased, other interesting Cat machines were purchased. The only restored non-Caterpillar item is Smith's perfect 1941 Farmall MD.

Alan Smith Excavating does much of its work for Ryan, Inc., a large construction contractor based in Janesville, Wisconsin. Both firms have been involved in the construction of Del Webb's 5,000-home Sun City–Huntley, Illinois. This is the latest of about a dozen Sun Cities across the country, developments catering to active adults fifty-five and older. July 1, 1998, was the official kick-off day for the village. Smith and several other members of the Antique Caterpillar Machinery Owner's Club displayed their washed and polished antique equipment for Phil Dion, Del Webb Chief Executive Officer, and 200 invited guests.

Right: Modern Caterpillar D7H
With a shorter roller frame than the low-ground-pressure (LGP) undercarriage version, the D7H weighed some 5,000 pounds (2,250 kg) less at a working weight of about 51,000 pounds (22,950 kg). The same 215-hp diesel was used in both. (Caterpillar, Inc.)

Below: Modern Caterpillar D10N
With a 1,649-ci (27,011-cc), V-12 engine of 520 hp, the D10N is capable of serious heavy work. It weighs about 122,000 pounds (54,900 kg) in working trim. (Caterpillar, Inc.)

Left: Modern Caterpillar D8N
The elevated drive sprocket design allowed for modular powertrain components for better serviceability. Also, the highly stressed drive elements were now up out of the mud and isolated from rough-ground shocks. The D8N sported a 285-hp engine. (Caterpillar, Inc.)

Below: Modern Caterpillar D7H LGP
The D7H with LGP undercarriage had a longer roller frame, extended both front and rear for nearly neutral weight distribution. This ensured grouser traction along the whole track even in soft conditions. The 56,000-pound (25,200-kg) machine had 215 flywheel hp. (Caterpillar, Inc.)

Above left: Caterpillar factory, 1999
A rare look inside the Track-type Tractor Division plant in East Peoria, Illinois. The tractor frame was mounted on a pneumatic skid, which lifted it from the floor so that the assembly could be moved down the assembly line.

Above right: Caterpillar factory, 1999
A Caterpillar V-8 diesel engine as delivered to the Track-type Tractor Division plant.

Left: Caterpillar factory, 1999
An assembly line view in the Track-type Tractor Division plant. The final drive and frame assembly of this crawler now had the ROPS installed.

Below: Caterpillar factory, 1999
Caterpillars on the assembly line. Note that different models were mixed on the line.

Caterpillar factory, 1999
Coming down the assembly line in the Track-type Tractor Division's plant, this crawler now had the engine installed. Rows of completed new Caterpillars wait at the end of the production line.

Caterpillar factory, 1999
A new D8 was loaded on a railroad flatcar for eventual delivery in Abu Dhabi, United Arab Emirates.

Caterpillar factory, 1999
This brand new D7 was on its way to the Ziegler dealership in Le Havre, France.

The Challenger Series

Over the last thirty years, the advent of the articulated four-wheel-drive tractor has taken over logging and farming jobs that were once the domain of the crawler. Construction projects still rely on tracked bulldozers, but rubber-tired vehicles have been taking over for loaders and towing jobs.

Caterpillar has not yielded the field, however. Five of the popular Caterpillar crawlers were offered in Special Application (SA) versions starting in 1966. But most importantly, a whole product line of Challenger farm tractors with the Mobil-trac system was launched. These were unique, all-purpose agricultural tractors with high-flotation rubber tracks.

The first production model was the Challenger 65, introduced in 1986. It combined the speed and mobility of rubber tires with the flotation and traction of tracks. Several years of design and testing preceded the Challenger 65. A prototype rubber-tracked D6 conversion was first, followed by a D3 and D4, and the 855X Series of six prototypes. The prototypes were eventually tested in the northern, southwestern, and western United States alongside four-wheel drives of all different makes. Successful testing led to the production Challenger 65 in 1987.

In the following years, variations on the original concept have been introduced. The Challenger 65B made its debut in 1991; the 65C followed as a 1993 model; and the 65D arrived in 1995. Larger and smaller Challengers have filled out the line: the 70C was introduced in 1993; the 75 in 1991; the 75C in 1993; the 85C in 1993; and the 85D in 1996. The line was filled out in 1994 by smaller, row-crop Challengers, the 35 and 45; these were joined in 1995 by the Model 55.

As of 1999, the Challenger row-crop tractors came in three power ratings: the 175-hp Challenger 35, 200-hp 45, and 225-hp 55. These were available in two widths: the standard, adjustable from 60 to 90 inches (150–225 cm); and the Wide-Track, adjustable between 80 and 120 inches (200–300 cm). These all featured a sixteen-speed, electronically controlled power-shift transmission with shuttle reverse in nine speeds. Top gear provided a 19.5 mph (31 kph) top speed. Five belt widths were available from 16 to 32 inches (40–80 cm) in two tread-bar styles. Hydro-mechanical differential steering allowed fingertip control via a conventional steering wheel. An ergonomically functional cab was equipped with an air-ride seat and an electronic control center monitor.

The 1999 conventional, non-row-crop Challengers were the E Series, which ranged from 310 to 410 hp. These were the fifth generation to follow the original Challenger 65 of 1987. Included in this series were the 310-hp Challenger 65E, 340-hp 75E, 375-hp 85E, and 410-hp 95E. Belt widths of 25, 30, and 35 inches (62.5, 75, and 87.5 cm) were available. The power-shift transmission had ten forward and two reverse speeds. Steering wheel–controlled hydro-mechanical differential steering made for effortless full-power turns. Finally, a completely modern cab with all the features rounded out these big-job tractors.

Getting into soft terrain with your big Challenger tractor did you no good unless you had an implement that would not sink in or compact the soil; Caterpillar announced its line of Versatile Flotation System (VFS) trailers. These could be adapted to hauling spray tanks or other heavy items, and were equipped with track belts similar to those of the Challenger tractors.

In 1997, an agreement was made between Caterpillar and the German company Claas KGaA of Harsewinkel, wherein Claas would market and service Challenger tractors in Europe through its dealer network. The European Challengers were the same as the Americans, except for the green-and-white Claas paint job.

Another new Cat item resulting from the Claas-Caterpillar agreement was the LEXION series of combines, introduced in late 1997. These come with rubber tracks like the Challengers or with rubber tires. This line represented a significant advance in separating technology. It also was automatically adjustable for hillside operation.

A Diversified Company

Since World War II, Caterpillar has been producing more than just tractors. In 1989, the name Caterpillar Tractor Company was changed to simply Caterpillar, Inc. Two new trademarks were adopted in 1989, Caterpillar and Cat. The company's products and services are readily identified by these two words. The trademarks incorporate a triangle under the "A" following the "C" in Caterpillar or Cat.

In 1990, Caterpillar reorganized itself into thirteen profit centers and four service divisions. Responsibility and accountability were moved downward to place key decision-making closer to the end product and the customer. Research continues in the basic scientific disciplines of metallurgy, electronics, ergonomics, sound control, and energy conversion. Cutting-edge computer-aided design (CAD) and manufacturing processes are in place.

The current product-line brochure shows a wide diversity of products, including track-type and wheeled tractors; forestry machines; track, wheeled, and backhoe loaders; trucks; articulated trucks; lift trucks; motor graders; excavators; engines; skidders; compaction equipment; landfill compactors; pipe layers; scrapers; pavement profilers; asphalt pavers; reclaimers and stabilizers; and tool carriers.

Above: Modern Caterpillar Challenger 65
The 65 was the original production Cat to use the high-flotation rubber-track system. The system greatly reduced soil compaction and improved traction, especially in soft soil conditions. (Caterpillar, Inc.)

Left, top: Modern Caterpillar Challenger 85D
The 85D offered 370 hp in gears five through ten. This was reduced by the onboard computer to 360 hp in gears three and four, and further reduced to 335 hp in first and second. This was done to reduce slippage and to lower torque stresses on final drive elements. Many operators never have occasion to use first or second. (Caterpillar, Inc.)

Left, bottom: Modern Caterpillar D4C
The D4C Series III bulldozer was a handy cleanup tool on a construction site. The 16,000-pound (7,200-kg) D4C had an 80-hp diesel engine. (Caterpillar, Inc.)

Modern Caterpillar D5C
The D5C Series III sported a 3046 diesel engine of 90 hp and weighed in at 18,500 pounds (8,325 kg). It was a little lighter and had about the same power as the 1940 D7 (7M). (Caterpillar, Inc.)

Following a long labor strike in the middle of the 1990s, Caterpillar management put in place a number of reforms designed to improve employee morale and productivity. During the 1990s, Caterpillar initiated its "Our Common Values" program, which gives people at all levels the freedom and the responsibility to discover new ways to solve problems.

Donald V. Fites was chairman and chief executive officer of Caterpillar, Inc., from 1990 to 1999. He was typical of the hands-on executives that made the company into the enviable organization that it is today. Fites had a civil engineering degree from Valparaiso University and was a Sloan Fellow at MIT. He was with Caterpillar for more than forty years and served sixteen years in overseas management positions, including marketing director of Caterpillar Mitsubishi, Ltd., in Tokyo, Japan, and president of Caterpillar Brazil S.A. in Sao Paulo, Brazil. Fites was active on other boards of directors, in community and church activities, and with the Salvation Army. In March 1999, Fites retired at age 65.

Caterpillar Executive Vice President Glen Barton succeeded Fites as CEO in 1999. Barton joined the company in 1961 with a degree in civil engineering from the University of Missouri. He has held positions in marketing and management both in the United States and overseas, including serving as president of Solar Turbines, Inc., a Caterpillar subsidiary.

Caterpillar is now a high-tech company that puts the highest priority on product support and customer service. Further, Caterpillar retains strong pride in its heritage.

Things have come full circle. Benjamin Holt, Daniel Best, and C. L. Best would be proud.

1998 Caterpillar Challenger 55 Row-Crop

With row spacing and power to match the needs of row-crop farming, the rubber-tracked Challenger was the ultimate farm tractor. Besides the 225-hp Challenger 55, the row-crop series also included the 175-hp Challenger 35 and 200-hp Challenger 45. (Caterpillar, Inc.)

1998 Caterpillar D3C

The smallest modern Cat, the D3C featured a 70-hp diesel engine. It weighed 15,500 pounds (6,975 kg). With a long undercarriage, The D3C was an excellent finish dozer. (Caterpillar, Inc.)

Modern Caterpillar Challenger 75

The big 300-hp 75 could make short work of chisel-plowing a large gumbo corn stubble field. (Caterpillar, Inc.)

Above: Modern Claas Challenger line

European Challengers were the same as the American models, except for the green-and-white Claas paint job. (Claas KGaA)

Right: Modern Claas Challenger cutaway

A cutaway illustration showing the workings of the latest Claas Challenger. (Claas KGaA)

Above: Modern Claas Challenger
A Claas Challenger works the harvest.
(Claas KGaA)

Left: Modern Claas Challenger
A Challenger labors through the night,
working the soil in a European field.
(Claas KGaA)

1997 Caterpillar Challenger 85D
Owner Duane Janikula has both an 85D and Challenger 65. He uses Challengers because of reduced compaction and greater traction than he could get with wheel tractors. He also commented on the comfort, convenience, and ease of operation afforded by the Challengers. Duane's wife Gloria routinely operates the Challengers.

Nebraska Tractor Test Results

In 1916 and 1917, Nebraska farmer Wilmot F. Crozier bought two tractors for his farm. The first was a Ford machine made not by Henry Ford, but by a Minneapolis company making a dubious effort to capitalize on Ford's famous name. The second was a three-wheeled Bull tractor also made in Minneapolis. Both were oversold and underdesigned failures. So, in 1918, Crozier bought a Rumely Three-Plow. The Rumely was a fine machine—indeed, it regularly pulled five plows without complaint.

In 1919, Crozier was elected to the Nebraska State Legislature, and as Representative Crozier, he teamed with Senator Charles Warner to introduce legislation in the 1919 session that resulted in the Nebraska Test Law requiring that any tractor sold in the state be certified that it met its advertised claims. The tests were to be conducted at the University of Nebraska in Lincoln by the Agricultural Engineering Department. L. W. Chase and Claude Shedd devised the tests and the test equipment. The law was passed, the test equipment created, and the test procedures written by fall 1919.

A Twin City 12/20 was the first candidate, but snowfall prevented completion of its tests. Thus, in spring 1920, a Waterloo Boy was the first to complete the test program successfully and receive a Nebraska certificate. Since then, most all tractors, large and small, have gone through Nebraska tests.

The highlights of the test results for Holt, Best, and Caterpillar machines are listed here.

Model	Year	Test #	Fuel Type	Belt/PTO Hp	Max. Drawbar Pull	Fuel Consumed	Weight
Holt Models							
Holt T-11	1920	59	Gas	36	5,558 lb	7.94	9,400 lb
Holt T-16	1920	61	Gas	57	9,756	7.16	18,500
Holt T-35	1922	86	Gas	28	3,275	9.45	4,040
Best Models							
Best Sixty	1921	76	Gas	56	11,000	8.05	17,500
Best Thirty	1921	77	Gas	30	4,343	6.68	7,400
Best Sixty	1923	98	Gas	66	11,295	7.22	18,580
Best Thirty	1923	99	Gas	33	4,930	7.40	8,100
Best Thirty	1924	104	Gas	38	7,563	9.28	9,065
Best Sixty	1924	105	Gas	73	12,360	7.68	20,000
Caterpillar Models							
Twenty	1928	150	Gas	29	5,721	7.04	7,822
Fifteen	1929	159	Gas	25	4,166	7.63	5,931
Ten	1929	160	Gas	18	2,816	7.93	4,575
Twenty-Five	1932	203	Gas	33	6,011	9.84	8,087
Fifty	1932	204	Gas	61	12,061	8.64	18,080
Twenty Flathead	1932	205	Gas	29	4,252	9.39	6,325
Thirty-Five	1932	206	Gas	44	8,169	9.05	12,380
Fifteen (Small)	1932	207	Gas	22	3,105	9.09	4,750

Model	Year	Test #	Fuel Type	Belt/PTO Hp	Max. Drawbar Pull	Fuel Consumed	Weight
Diesel	1932	208	Diesel	77	11,991	13.87	25,860
Sixty-Five	1932	209	Gas	84	13,597	8.28	24,965
Seventy	1933	213	Gas	82	16,796	8.13	30,800
Diesel Fifty	1933	214	Diesel	66	12,765	14.12	20,125
Diesel Thirty-Five	1933	217	Diesel	45	9,135	13.49	14,720
Diesel Seventy-Five	1933	218	Diesel	93	18,697	14.62	30,050
R5	1934	224	Gas	59	10,384	9.64	13,675
R2	1934	225	Gas	32	5,274	8.78	7,420
Twenty-Two	1934	226	Distillate	31	4,534	8.1	6,210
R3	1934	227	Gas	42	7,622	9.05	10,029
Twenty-Two	1934	228	Gas	31	4,900	9.11	6,210
Diesel Fifty	1935	240	Diesel	72	13,000	14.24	20,790
Diesel Forty	1935	243	Diesel	56	9,692	14.18	15,642
Forty	1935	244	Gas	56	9,496	9.24	13,625
RD7	1936	255	Diesel	96	16,782	15.09	21,020
RD8	1936	256	Diesel	118	20,485	14.41	33,690
Thirty	1936	271	Distillate	34	6,120	9.01	9,975
RD4	1936	273	Diesel	40	7,852	13.83	10,100
D8	1939	314	Diesel	110	26,110	15.86	32,925
R2	1939	320	Gas	29	5,676	8.33	6,835
D2	1939	322	Diesel	30	5,903	13.32	7,420
D8	1940	357	Diesel	128	26,208	15.02	35,000
D7	1940	358	Diesel	89	21,351	14.81	24,790
D6	1941	374	Diesel	78	16,674	14.57	17,750
D6	1949	416	Diesel	77	16,222	14.28	18,805
D2	1949	418	Diesel	36	6,778	13.63	7,255
D2	1955	553	Diesel	42	7,413	12.93	8,536
D4	1955	554	Diesel	59	9,976	13.94	12,531
D6	1955	555	Diesel	93	17,486	14.13	20,765
D7	1956	582	Diesel	122	26,286	15.39	30,460
D4	1960	746	Diesel	57	11,694	13.12	14,825
Challenger 65E	1998	1748	Diesel	309	33,284	20.6	34,360

Notes on test data:

Fuel: When Caterpillar brought its first diesel tractor for testing (test number 208), diesel fuel was not available and the test was run on number 2 furnace oil. Diesel fuel was available for subsequent tests.

Belt Hp: Either measured at the belt pulley or at the PTO. Test D, maximum.

Drawbar Pull: Maximum drawbar pull obtainable in pounds. Test G.

Fuel Consumption: The rate of fuel consumption in horsepower hours per gallon. Higher numbers are better.

Weight: The weight of the tractor, operator, and ballast.

Tractors tested are certified by the manufacturer to be stock machines, conforming to the specifications submitted with the test application.

Bibliography

The following books offered essential background on Caterpillar's origins and history.

Baldwin, Nick, and Andrew Morland. *Classic Tractors of the World*. Stillwater, Minnesota: Voyageur Press, 1998.

Caterpillar Tractor Company. *Fifty Years on Tracks*. Peoria, Illinois: Caterpillar, 1954.

Caterpillar, Inc. *The Caterpillar Story*. Peoria, Illinois: Caterpillar, Inc., n.d.

Cochrane, Willard W. *The Development of American Agriculture: A Historical Analysis*. Minneapolis, Minnesota: University of Minnesota Press, 1993.

Creighton, Jeff J. *Combines and Harvesters Photographic History*. Osceola, Wisconsin: Motorbooks International, 1996.

Gray, R. B. *The Agricultural Tractor 1855–1950*. Saint Joseph, Michigan: American Society of Agricultural Engineers, 1975 revised edition.

LaVoie, Bob. *Caterpillar Gas Tractor Restoration and Interchange Manual*. Osceola, Wisconsin: Motorbooks International, 1996.

Leffingwell, Randy. *Caterpillar*. Osceola, Wisconsin: Motorbooks International, 1994.

Longfoot, Peter J. *Caterpillar Tractors 1926–1959*. N.p.: Peter J. Longfoot, n.d.

Mills, Robert K., ed. I*mplement & Tractor: Reflections on 100 Years of Farm Equipment*. Overland Park, Kansas: Intertec Publishing Corp., 1986.

Orlemann, Eric C. *Caterpillar*. Osceola, Wisconsin: Motorbooks International, 1998.

Payne, Walter A., ed. *Benjamin Holt: The Story of the Caterpillar Tractor*. Stockton, California: University of the Pacific, 1982.

Pripps, Robert N., and Andrew Morland. *The Field Guide to Vintage Farm Tractors*. Stillwater, Minnesota: Voyageur Press, 1999.

Sanders, Ralph W. *Vintage Farm Tractors*. Stillwater, Minnesota: Voyageur Press, 1996.

Stephens, Randy, ed. *Farm Tractors 1926–1956*. Overland Park, Kansas: Intertec Publishing Corp., 1990. A compilation of pages from *The Cooperative Tractor Catalog* and *The Red Tractor Book*.

Upson, William Hazlett. *Alexander Botts—Earthworm Tractors*. New York: Pocket Books, 1946.

Upson, William Hazlett. *Earthworms Through the Ages: The Wisdom of Alexander Botts*. New York. Rinehart and Co., 1947.

Upson, William Hazlett. *The Best of Botts*. New York: David McKay Company, 1961.

Wendel, C. H. *Nebraska Tractor Tests Since 1920*. Osceola, Wisconsin: Motorbooks International/ Crestline Publishing, 1986.

Wik, Reynold M. *Benjamin Holt & Caterpillar: Tracks and Combines*. Saint Joseph, Michigan: American Society of Agricultural Engineers, 1984.

Young, James A., and Jerry D. Budy. *Endless Tracks in the Woods*. Osceola, Wisconsin: Motorbooks International/Crestline Publishing, 1989.

Zinman, Michael. *The History of the Decline and Fall of the Caterpillar Tractor Company: A Modern Business Saga*. Ardsley, New York: Haydn Foundation, 1986.

1934 Caterpillar Diesel Seventy-Five
The Diesel Seventy-Five was made from 1933 to 1935. It was an outgrowth of the Diesel Seventy, which was made only in 1933. With minor changes, it became the RD8. Owner: Larry Simon.

Index

About the Authors

Author Robert Pripps stands alongside Marv Fery's Caterpillar Ten.

Robert N. Pripps was born in 1932 on a small farm in northern Wisconsin. Besides farming, his father did local road building and maintenance with a JT crawler and Russell grader. Hard times during the Great Depression put an end to both the farming and road construction, and Bob's dad went to work as a Wisconsin Conservation Department Forest Ranger, a job that he held for the next thirty-five years. Living at the ranger station, Bob was always exposed to trucks and tractors. His first driving experience came at age nine when he disked a fire lane with an Allis-Chalmers crawler. During summers throughout World War II, Bob worked on neighboring farms, earning the opportunity to drive one farmer's new Farmall H at age eleven.

Bob's curiosity with things mechanical almost cost him his life at age twelve. He got a mitten caught in the power takeoff of a Gallion road grader. He extricated himself from the machine before it killed him, but the encounter cost him his right thumb.

At age fourteen came another life-changing event: his best friend's father bought the first Ford-Ferguson tractor in the area. Abject envy is not a pretty thing, but that's what reigned in Bob's heart. It was in no way sated until Bob got his own 2N at age fifty.

Bob went to high school in Eagle River, Wisconsin, earning his private pilot's license by graduation in 1950. His missing right thumb kept him from military service, so he attended Parks Air College to study engineering and receive a commercial pilot's license and multi-engine rating. To help support himself, Bob took a night job at McDonnel Aircraft in St. Louis. Marriage and family responsibilities soon made the job a priority and schooling secondary. Bob became a flight test engineer on the RF-101 Voodoo while continuing night and correspondence school. Subsequent jobs in test engineering included Atlas missile base activation for General Dynamics and jet engine starter and constant speed drive testing for the Sundstrand Corporation.

After seventeen years of part-time classes, Bob graduated from college in 1969 with a Bachelor of Science in Marketing. Bob also held a certificate in Aeronautical Engineering by that time. He then served as the marketing manager for Sundstrand's Dayton, Ohio, office, retiring at age fifty-five.

Along the way, Bob inherited thirty acres of maple forest that were part of the Wisconsin farm on which he was born. That's when he found justification for the Ford-Ferguson 2N that helps with harvesting sap for maple syrup. He later added a 1948 John Deere Model B to the farm.

After retiring, Bob began writing a book on his favorite tractor, the Ford. The book was published in 1990, teaming Bob with renowned English automotive photographer Andrew Morland. Since then, Bob and Andrew have collaborated on ten books on classic tractors, and Bob has authored five other tractor titles on his own.

Bob and his wife Janice now live in northern Wisconsin, almost within sight of the original homestead. Besides steady work on books, Bob and one of his three sons make about 150 gallons of maple syrup each spring.

Andrew Morland was educated in Great Britain. He completed one year at Taunton College of Art in Somerset and then three years at London College of Printing studying photography. He has worked since graduation as a freelance photojournalist, traveling throughout Europe and North America. His work has been published in numerous magazines and books. He is also the photographer of Voyageur Press's *Classic Tractors of the World, Vintage Ford Tractors,* and *The Field Guide to Vintage Farm Tractors.* His interests include tractors, machinery, old motorbikes, and cars. He lives in a thatched cottage in Somerset, Great Britain, that was built in the 1680s. He is married and has one daughter.